Books by Erskine Caldwell

ALL NIGHT LONG, 1942 • ALL-OUT ON THE ROAD TO SMOLENSK, 1942 • AMERICAN EARTH, 1930 • THE BASTARD, 1929 • CALL IT EXPERIENCE, 1951 • CERTAIN WOMEN, 1957 • CLAUDELLE INGLISH, 1959 • THE COURTING OF SUSIE BROWN, 1952 • EPISODE IN PALMETTO, 1950 • GEORGIA BOY, 1943 • GOD'S LITTLE ACRE, 1933 • GRETTA, 1955 • GULF COAST STORIES, 1956 • A HOUSE IN THE UPLANDS, 1946 • JOURNEYMAN, 1935 • KNEEL TO THE RISING SUN, 1935 • A LAMP FOR NIGHTFALL, 1952 • LOVE AND MONEY, 1954 • MOSCOW UNDER FIRE, 1942 • PLACE CALLED ESTHERVILLE, 1949 • POOR FOOL, 1929 • SOME AMERICAN PEOPLE, 1935 • SOUTHWAYS, 1938 • THE SURE HAND OF GOD, 1947 • THIS VERY EARTH, 1948 • TOBACCO ROAD, 1932 • TRAGIC GROUND, 1944 • TROUBLE IN JULY, 1940 • WE ARE THE LIVING, 1933 • WHEN YOU THINK OF ME, 1959

For Children

MOLLY COTTONTAIL, 1958

Anthologies of Erskine Caldwell

THE COMPLETE STORIES OF ERSKINE CALDWELL, 1953 • THE HUMOROUS SIDE, EDITED BY ROBERT CANTWELL, 1951 • STORIES, EDITED BY HENRY SEIDEL CANBY, 1944

By Erskine Caldwell and Margaret Bourke-White

NORTH OF THE DANUBE, 1939 • RUSSIA AT WAR, 1942 • SAY! IS THIS THE U.S.A.? 1940 • YOU HAVE SEEN THEIR FACES, 1937

WHEN YOU THINK OF ME

When You Think of Me

BY

ERSKINE CALDWELL

With illustrations by Louis Macouillard

LITTLE, BROWN AND COMPANY

Boston  Toronto

Published simultaneously in Canada
by Little, Brown & Company (Canada) Limited

PRINTED IN THE UNITED STATES OF AMERICA

To
Virginia Moffett Caldwell

CONTENTS

THE STORIES

The Light

THE GANG of schoolboys from town passed down the road early in the evening. It was a fairly warm night in late fall, and the boys, bareheaded and shouting, were wandering over the countryside surrounding the town, keeping a safe distance from the policemen, and celebrating a football victory. When the group of boys passed Mrs. Wilkins' house, they stopped and threw a dozen or more rocks at the small, one-story, unpainted cottage.

Little old Mrs. Wilkins went to the door and stood peering out into the darkness. The group of boys watched her for a few minutes, and then one of them, in a husky voice, shouted Charlie's name as loudly as he could.

Mrs. Wilkins ran back into the room, picked up the lamp that she always kept lighted by the window, and carried it into the front yard. While the boys watched her from the road, Mrs. Wilkins began looking for

Charlie all around the house. She held the lamp high over her head so she could see where she was going without stumbling. After looking all around the house, she stopped and listened for any sound she could hear. Then she called her son's name several times.

"Charlie! Oh, Charlie! Where are you, Charlie-boy?"

The lamp sputtered a little when a breeze suddenly swept across the yard, and the chimney became smoked around the top. By that time the boys had gone down the road out of sight and hearing distance. Mrs. Wilkins' hand had begun to shake and tremble, and she looked up at the lamp held high above her head just in time to steady the chimney with her free hand and to keep it from falling off and breaking on the ground.

She searched the back yard carefully and the front yard again and even walked around in the nearby field during the next half hour. Finally, after once going as far as the road, she went back into the house and closed the door and put the lamp on the table beside the window.

After she had cleaned the blackened chimney, she sat down in her chair and drew her woolen shawl around her shoulders. Then she began talking to herself a little, stopping every once in a while to listen for any sound she might hear, and to glance hopefully out the window.

All the neighbors had tried at one time or another

during the past nine years to tell Mrs. Wilkins in the kindest possible way that Charlie Wilkins would never come back. But no, Charlie was her son, and she was convinced that he would come home sooner or later. Nobody in the neighborhood could make her believe anything else.

"The boy had an accident, Mrs. Wilkins," one of the neighbors had told her again only the week before, "and he won't ever be coming back home."

Mrs. Wilkins shook her head disbelievingly as she had always done. She could not believe anything the neighbors tried to tell her. Charlie was all she had ever had in the world since the day he was born, and as far as she was concerned he would always be alive.

Eleven years before, Charlie Wilkins had left home and gone to Akron, where he had found a job in a rubber factory. Two years later the chief of police in town received a message from Akron which said that Charlie Wilkins had fallen into a chemical vat, and that before his body could be found and removed, it had been dissolved in the solution. There were no remains to ship back to his mother, and for that reason she had never believed he was dead.

"Charlie was twenty years old when he left home," she had told everybody who tried to make her understand that he was no longer alive, "and if he comes home tonight, he will be thirty-one years old. He will be a big strong grown man, with thick black hair and blue eyes just like his father had. When Charlie left home to go to work in Akron, he had not filled out all over, but when he comes back, he will be as big and strong as his father was at that age. But even if he has changed, I'll know Charlie when he comes back home to see me. He couldn't change too much to fool me."

She sat in her chair by the window, her hands folded in her lap, listening and waiting. Occasionally she would close her eyes for several moments, and then, afraid that she had been asleep, look anxiously out the window into the night.

"My boy wouldn't forget to come back to see me," she said to herself. "If everybody in the whole world came in here and tried to tell me he wasn't coming home, I wouldn't believe a single word of it, because Charlie told me he was coming back to see me as soon as he got a chance to leave his job for a while, and Charlie never told me a fib in his whole life, not even when he was a little fellow running around the yard trying to catch sparrows with a spoonful of salt, because every time I asked him if he had done such and such a thing, he always told me the truth and looked me straight in the eyes while he was saying it. Charlie has always been a truthful boy."

The Light

The clock over the fireplace struck ten. Mrs. Wilkins looked at the clock, and then she turned her head so she would be able to look out the window. It was not late for her to be up, because she was in the habit of staying awake until after eleven, sometimes far past midnight, waiting.

An automobile came slowly up the road. Mrs. Wilkins sat up erectly while she listened to the sound of the car. When it reached the front of the house, it did not stop but continued up the road.

"Charlie's coming home sometime," she said to herself. "He'll come in an automobile, or he'll come walking. He said he was coming back, and he'll come one way or another. I don't know why people are always trying to make me believe he isn't coming back to see me."

She suddenly sat up, gripping the arms of the chair, when she thought she heard a sound. The sound was like the squeak her chair sometimes made, but it sounded to her as though it came from outside the house — like the squeak of the gate in the front yard.

Before she could make up her mind about the sound, there was a knock at the door. Mrs. Wilkins gripped her hands tightly. She did not know what to make of it. Nobody ever came to see her so late at night, and she did not know what to do. While she sat there, her body

7

trembling, the knock on the door was heard again. This time she jumped excitedly to her feet.

"It's Charlie!" she cried.

It was all she could do to keep from weeping. She ran to the closet where she kept her Sunday clothes tied up in a box. Nervously she ripped away the cord. The tears that she tried to hold back suddenly filled her eyes and blinded her. She could not see anything she tried to do. She felt her way out of the closet and tried to take off her housedress.

At that moment she heard the knock on the door for the third time. She knew then that the knock was real. She had heard it three times, and the sound was unmistakable. She finally was able to change her dress, and then she took off her house shoes and put on one of her Sunday slippers. She dropped the other slipper somewhere, but she did not have time to look for it.

"I'm coming — I'm coming — I'm coming!" she cried, pinning up her hair with one hand while she tried to fasten her Sunday dress with the other. "Charlie, I'm coming! I'm coming, Charlie-boy!"

When the dress was fastened, she still could not find her other slipper. She could not find it anywhere, even though she remembered dropping it on the floor in her haste.

"You did come back, didn't you, Charlie? I knew you would, because you said you would!"

She ran around the room, stopping to pick up the lamp, and looked under the chairs and bed for the slipper.

"Oh Charlie, you did come back, didn't you!"

At last she found the slipper and put it on. Then she took the lamp and went as quickly as she could to the door.

"Charlie! Charlie-boy! I just knew you would come back to see me! I always knew you would!"

When she reached the door, her trembling hands fumbled with the latch. She put the lamp on the floor and tried to open the door with both hands.

"Are you still there, Charlie?" she called loudly.

"I'm right here, Ma!"

"Oh Charlie-boy, I'm so glad!"

"Why don't you open the door and let me in, Ma?" the voice asked.

"Oh my boy, my boy!" she cried.

At last she managed to turn the latch and open the door. Then she turned around, picked up the lamp, and stepped on the threshold.

"Where are you, Charlie?" she called.

She stood in the doorway, lamp in hand, looking all

around the yard. She could not see anybody. The yard was as empty and bare as it had ever been.

"Where are you, Charlie?" she asked frantically. "Charlie, where are you?"

When she stepped to the ground, somebody jumped into view from the corner of the house.

"Here I am, Ma!" he said. The figure came toward her with hat pulled down over the face and with collar turned up. "Don't you know me, Ma?"

"Charlie-boy, is that you?" she said excitedly. "Come close and let me see you, son!"

A boy stepped up in front of her, standing directly in the light shining from the lamp in her hand.

Mrs. Wilkins' face looked as if a sudden, unbearable pain had struck her. She tottered from side to side until it seemed as if she would fall to the ground.

"You are not Charlie!" she said painfully.

The group of boys at the fence suddenly broke into loud laughter. They had been up the road overturning farm carts and driving cows out of pastures, and when they came back to Mrs. Wilkins' house, one of them, Ben Sears, told the other boys to watch him play a joke on the old woman. The group of boys had hidden behind a hedge where they could see and hear everything that took place.

The Light

"You're not Charlie!" Mrs. Wilkins said again as tears filled her eyes. "You're not my Charlie-boy!"

Jerking off his hat, Ben Sears turned and ran out of the yard. He and the other boys disappeared in the darkness as they ran down the road.

Mrs. Wilkins stood in the yard for a long time after they had left, still holding the lamp high over her head.

"Oh Charlie, it wasn't you!" she said to herself, her words partly distinct, partly inaudible. "Why couldn't it have been you, Charlie-boy? I've waited so long!"

After a while Mrs. Wilkins walked slowly across the yard and went into the house. There she closed and locked the door, and then began taking off her Sunday clothes. When she had finished folding the clothes and putting them carefully into the box in the closet, she carried the lamp to the table by the window. As she had always done, she was careful to put the lamp in its accustomed place so as much light as possible would shine through the window. Then she adjusted the wick so the flame would be bright and clear and not smoke the chimney. When she was satisfied that the light would be bright and clear, she started across the room to her bed. She was in the middle of the room when she fell heavily to the floor.

When she fell, she did not know whether she had

tripped on the rug, or whether it was her strength that gave out and let her fall. As she lay there the last thing she thought was that she would have to get up in time to open the door for Charlie when he came home.

A Visit to Mingus County

IT WAS not long after midnight when Guthrie Rankin knocked on the front door of Rance Rankin's house in Mingus County.

The summer evening had been warm and humid since sunset, and a bright yellow moon was shining, and, since both Uncle Rance and Aunt Biddie were light sleepers, they woke up right away. Uncle Rance, groaning and complaining for all of his sixty years, got out of his bed and looked through the window, but it was too dark in the shadow of the porch roof to see who was there at that time of night.

"Who in the world is that, Rance?" Aunt Biddie, turning over with a squeaking of the springs, asked in a mutter from her bed on the other side of the room. "What could anybody want at this unearthly hour?"

"There's no way of telling from here, Biddie," he answered. "I'll have to go to the front door to find out."

"Whoever it is," she said, her voice becoming shrill, "I

don't want any of my potted geraniums on the front porch knocked over. I've spent all summer nursing them along to blooming, and I want every single one of them to stay that way. Do you hear me, Rance?"

"I heard you, Biddie," he answered.

When Uncle Rance got to the front door, he saw a tall, round-faced, unusually fleshy man standing on the porch and holding a small satchel in his hand. There was a large automobile gleaming in the moonlight in front of the house. As closely as Uncle Rance could tell in the dim light, the stranger appeared to be about thirty-five or forty years old and probably weighed as much as two hundred and fifty pounds.

"Howdy," he said. "Are you Uncle Rance?"

"I'm Rance Rankin," Uncle Rance answered cautiously.

"Well, that's fine and dandy," the stranger said in a booming voice, dropping the satchel to the floor. He got a firm grip on Uncle Rance's hand and shook it up and down. "I'm Cousin Guthrie Rankin from New Orleans. How are you, Uncle Rance? I've been driving over these gumbo roads and sorghum fields for the past three hours looking for your house, and I'm sure glad I found it at last." He finally released Uncle Rance's hand. "But maybe you don't know exactly who I am, Uncle Rance. I'm Tom Rankin's oldest son. I'm Guthrie Rankin.

This is the first time I've been back here to Mingus County in about ten years, and I don't know my way around very well. That's why it took me so long to find your place."

"Which Tom Rankin are you talking about?" Uncle Rance asked him. "There've been three Tom Rankins in the family in my lifetime, and maybe some others that I don't even know about, besides."

"Dad was the one who went to New Orleans about forty years ago and started a pottery and tile business. After Dad died, I took over the business, and I've been running it ever since. We make all kinds of flowerpots and roofing tile and things like that."

"That particular Rankin was a first cousin of mine," Uncle Rance said, nodding his head. "He's the one who's been dead and buried about ten or eleven years now. I'd have gone to his funeral when he was buried in Antioch cemetery, but I was busy grinding sorghum at the time and couldn't afford to take the time off. Are you looking for his gravestone?"

"Not exactly," Guthrie told him, kicking the satchel closer to the door. "I came to visit living relations and get all the facts and information I can about the family. I've decided it would be a good idea to get together a family history of the Rankins, and I figured that Mingus County would be the best place to start. Dad used to say that there were more Rankins in Mingus County than in the rest of the world put together."

"I don't know about that, but there sure are a heap of us in Mingus County, both living and dead," Uncle Rance said. "The fact is, there's so many Rankins in Mingus County that I can't always recall how I'm kin to who, most of the time. What I generally do is just claim kin with anybody with the name of Rankin, and let it go at that. Where are you aiming to stay while you're visiting relatives and finding out about the family tree?"

"Just here and there," Guthrie said, laughing a little. "First with one relation and then another. By doing that, none of my kinfolks could say I showed favoritism to a particular relation and maybe found out some family secrets that somebody was trying to cover up and hide. Now, if you've got a spare bed for the rest of the night, I'd sure appreciate using it, because it's a little late in the night now to be doing any more family visiting. After a good sleep, I'll start out again early in the morning and look for some skeletons in the closet." He chuckled to himself for a moment. "A family history would be mighty dull reading if there wasn't a little scandal scattered through it."

With a quick glance at Guthrie, Uncle Rance began nodding his head.

"I've always prided myself on having a spare bed for

a relative. And since you're a Rankin, you're welcome to it. Come on inside the house."

Uncle Rance went down the hall and turned on the light in the spare bedroom. Carrying his small satchel, Guthrie followed. When they were inside the room, Uncle Rance took a good look at Guthrie.

"There's no doubt about it," Uncle Rance said, squinting his eyes in the bright light. "You do have a real family resemblance. It shows up on you, all right. Nearly all Rankins, no matter which branch of the family they belong to, have ears that stick out like yours do, and a heap of them have curly brown hair like yours, too. And I'm yet to see a Rankin who didn't have big feet." Uncle Rance shook his head slowly from side to side after that. "But I don't recall a single, solitary Rankin carrying as much weight as you do, though. Even the women in the family didn't go that much to fat."

Guthrie laughed until his sagging jowls quivered and his round belly shook up and down. He was still laughing when he took off his coat and hung it on the back of a chair. He looked even fatter in his shirtsleeves.

"Uncle Rance," he said, turning around, "maybe I get my robust health from my mother's side of the family. All the Dickinsons —"

"You don't have to tell me about the Dickinsons,"

Uncle Rance spoke up. "I've never known your Aunt Biddie to weigh less than two hundred, and right now I'd guess she's on the far side of two hundred and fifty."

Uncle Rance turned around and went to the door.

"It's getting late in the night," he said, "and I reckon we'd both better get some sleep before daybreak. We can do some more talking about family traits in the morning."

After leaving the room, he went down the hall and locked the front door. As he was getting into his bed, Aunt Biddie called to him across the room.

"Who was that, Rance?" she asked sharply.

"That was Cousin Guthrie Rankin from New Orleans," he told her.

Aunt Biddie was silent for a while, and then she suddenly turned over in her bed with a loud squeaking of the springs.

"You can let him claim kin to you, if you want to," she said severely in her shrill, high-pitched voice, "but he's no relation of mine. I'm a Rankin by marriage only, and that's all I'll admit to as long as I live and breathe. I'm a Dickinson by birth, and proud of it, but beyond that I'll pick and choose who I want to be related to. I'm glad you sent him on his way, wherever it is he's going."

Uncle Rance closed his eyes and tried to go to sleep, but he remained as wide awake as ever. After that he looked at the moonlight shining through the window and wondered what Aunt Biddie would say if she knew that Guthrie was still in the house. In the quiet of the night he was certain he could hear Guthrie snoring in the spare bedroom.

Aunt Biddie, with a powerful heave of her fleshy body, sat upright in her bed.

"Rance," she said excitedly, "that's the no-account Rankin we're always hearing about. I'm as sure of it as I know I live and breathe."

"Now, Biddie," Uncle Rance said soothingly, "don't go and get upset over a little thing like that. It's only natural that a family as big as ours is going to have a black sheep in it once in a while. That's the kind of thing that has to be taken for granted — like a time of rainfall and a time of sunshine. On the other hand, just look at all the fine upstanding Rankins there are in Mingus County, and elsewhere in the world, too. I don't mind saying I'm as proud as proud can be of the Rankins, by and large."

"Maybe being a Rankin is good enough for you," Aunt Biddie said, "but as long as I live and breathe I'll be thankful I was born a Dickinson."

"The Dickinsons are fine people, too, Biddie," he told

her. "I've always admired the Dickinsons, by and large."

Aunt Biddie was quiet for a long time after that, but just when Uncle Rance thought she had gone to sleep at last, she got to her feet and stood in the middle of the room.

"Wake up, Rance!" she called loudly. "Wake up right away!"

"What's the matter now, Biddie?" he asked fearfully.

"What was Guthrie Rankin doing here? What did he come here for?"

"He said he's going to get together a family history of the Rankins. He came all the way from New Orleans just to talk to relatives and get all the facts and information he can about the family. It's a mighty fine thing for him to take the trouble to do."

"That's Tom Rankin's son!" she said, the room resounding with her excited, high-pitched voice. "I know who he is now! Tom Rankin and my sister! It was the most outrageous thing that ever happened in my family! I'll never live long enough to get over the shame of it!"

"Now, Biddie," Uncle Rance said soothingly, trying to get her to be calm, "all that happened far back in the past — forty or more years ago in the past. It's not the kind of thing to carry a grudge about, anyway. Guthrie

Rankin didn't have a thing in the world to do with that
— he wasn't even born at the time."

"Maybe he wasn't born then, but he's alive now, and
he came back here to Mingus County to dig up the
past."

Uncle Rance, groaning weakly, got out of bed and
turned on the light. He knew he could not go to sleep
after that. He sat on the side of his bed, holding his
head in his hands, and tried to think what he could
do. Aunt Biddie began pinning up her hair in a tight
knot.

"If that Guthrie Rankin comes back here again and
tries to pry into my past life," she said threateningly,
"I'll call the sheriff and have him put in jail. That's
something I won't stand for — kin or no kin!"

Uncle Rance got to his feet and put on his shirt and
pants. He knew he would not get another wink of sleep
until something could be done about Guthrie Rankin.
He looked at the clock on the table. It was nearly three
o'clock, and dawn would be breaking in less than two
hours. When he had finished dressing, he looked across
the room at Aunt Biddie.

"Biddie," he began fearfully, "Biddie, I might as well
go ahead and tell you what happened, but I want you to
be calm about it."

She turned to him with a piercing look.

"Is that scoundrelly Rankin under this roof — did you invite him to sleep in the spare bedroom?"

Uncle Rance nodded without looking at her.

"I thought so!" she said sharply. "Something was telling me to be suspicious!"

"What are you going to do, Biddie?" he asked.

"I'm going to stand over you till you put him out of this house — that's what. Nobody's coming here and dig up the scandalous past as long as I live and breathe. Now, go in there and tell Guthrie Rankin to get out of that bed and be on his way."

"But, Biddie," Uncle Rance pleaded, "you ought to be reasonable. It's three o'clock in the morning, and nobody ought to be made to get up out of his sleep like that — Rankin or no Rankin."

"Anybody who comes around here trying to dig up the past deserves to be put out," she told Uncle Rance. "Now, get him out of this house like I told you."

"I hate to do a thing like that to a relative of mine, Biddie," he protested. "It's just not the right thing to do. Now, if he wasn't a Rankin — born and bred —"

Aunt Biddie did not say another word. She merely stood there glaring at him.

Uncle Rance went down the hall and opened the door of the spare bedroom. After listening to Guthrie snore for several moments, Uncle Rance went to the bed and shook him until he was awake.

"I sure hate to have to tell you, Guthrie," Uncle Rance said, "but something's come up that I didn't foresee, and you'll have to get up and put your clothes on."

"Why do I have to do that?" Guthrie asked sleepily.

"Because your Aunt Biddie has made up her mind for you to go visit some other relatives. She says for you to get up and go right away."

"Before it's even daylight?"

"That's what she says."

"But there'll be plenty of time to do that after breakfast, Uncle Rance."

"The way she feels about it, there won't be any breakfast — for you, or me either, if you don't leave."

Rubbing his eyes, Guthrie got out of bed and began putting on his clothes. Uncle Rance waited in the hall, glancing back and forth at Aunt Biddie standing in the doorway and at Guthrie stumbling around sleepily in the spare bedroom. When Guthrie came out of the room with his small satchel and walked heavily down the hall, he smiled at Aunt Biddie.

"Good morning, Aunt Biddie," he said as he went toward the front door.

"You can keep your good-mornings to yourself," she told him curtly.

27

Guthrie stopped and looked at her for a moment.

"Aunt Biddie, what's the matter?" he asked.

Uncle Rance pushed Guthrie through the doorway to the front porch, down the steps, and across the yard toward his automobile. When they reached the car, Guthrie tossed his satchel into the back seat.

"I've never been treated like this before by kinfolks," he said, shaking his head. "Aunt Biddie acts like she is no kin at all."

"And she's been no kin to me either, for forty years," Uncle Rance told him, lowering his voice to a whisper. "If you'd lived in the same house with a woman that long and she'd never warmed your bed even once, you wouldn't claim much kinship with her either."

"How did that come about, Uncle Rance?"

"Spite — nothing but spite. Long before we got married, she found out she could never get pregnant, but her sister could — your mother — and did. That's how I happen to be your real father, son. Your Aunt Biddie's two brothers held a shotgun at my back and made me marry her, and that's why your mother had to hurry up and marry Tom Rankin. Now, when you write up the family history, son, I want you to be sure and put down the true facts."

Aunt Biddie came to the front porch.

"Rance!" she called in a loud voice. "You listen to

me! Quit that gossiping with a total stranger and come back in the house this very minute!"

"All right, Biddie," he said. Smiling, he reached forward and gripped Guthrie's arm for a moment. "I'm coming, Biddie."

As he walked toward the front porch, he listened to the sound of the engine when Guthrie started his car and drove away into the night. It was the most pleasing sound he had heard in a long time.

The Story of Mahlon

"MAHLON," they would say, "Mahlon, you should go and find yourself a wife. A man like you ought to take a wife and leave children in the world when your days are finished."

"A wife? Ho! Ho! Ho! Me? A wife?"

"Certainly," they would tell him. "You have your farm here, and a comfortable house — a wife and children would not be a hardship on you. Mahlon, just stop and think what a joy it would be to have a fine woman here to love you and children to play in the meadow."

"Me? A wife? Why, I have no time for things like that! Just look at all the land around me — I've got all that to care for. My fields need me night and day. I have no time for women and children. I would never wish to have them here."

Mahlon would walk into one of the fields and pick up a handful of soil and hold it while he looked at the plowed ground all around him. He would hold the soil for a long time, caressing it with his broad fingers as though it were too tender for him to squeeze in his hand. After a while he would drop to his knees and lay the soil carefully in its place.

"Don't you remember what the Holy Bible says in such and such a place, Mahlon?" they would ask. "The Bible says: 'Male and female created He them.'"

"Well, what does that mean? I've read the Bible, but I've never thought that passage was meant for me to ponder over."

"That means, Mahlon, that we were made male and female," they would say, "and that the two should live in a house together. No house is built for one alone. You should go and find yourself a wife, Mahlon. It is meant for you to take a wife."

Mahlon walked away with his sack of shelled corn. When he reached the newly plowed ground, he took out a handful of seed and dropped them into the mellow earth. Each time he dropped a seed he got down on his knees and pressed it into the warm earth until it was fully covered. He walked along the furrow, stooping down to put his hands into the warm earth and closing his eyes while he felt the warmth of the earth surge through his body.

There were times when neighbors would come and tell him that there was no need for the few ears of corn that he grew and that he should go to the city and work in a factory. Mahlon laughed at them for being so foolish.

"You are a fool, Mahlon," they would say. "In the city you would be much happier. There are many things to do there, and there are hundreds of people to talk to. Come to your senses, Mahlon, and get yourself a job in the city."

"I wouldn't like that. In the city the streets are hard, and there is no earth to feel. When the spring comes, there would be no place for me to plant seed. Wouldn't I look the fool dropping seed on the hard streets! Here on the earth when spring comes, I drop the seed into the mellow soil and take care of them while they are sprouting and growing. In the city there would be no soil for the seed; the streets are hard in the city, and the walls of the factories keep out the sun and rain. I must have sun and rain to fall upon me."

"You are a foolish man, Mahlon," they would say. "The earth cares nothing for you. You are wasting your life here. The earth is just as well off without seed as it is with seed. The earth does not love you as you think it does. You are making a fool of yourself to be laughed at, Mahlon."

Mahlon would walk away, going out of sight where he could lie down on the earth and press his face upon it. He would lie there on the ground with his arms and

legs outspread and feel the mellow soil against his face
and the warmth of the earth flowing through his body.

But the people would not leave him alone. They came
running across the fields looking for him, tramping ruth-
lessly on the sprouting seed that he had so carefully
pressed into the earth. With each step they scarred the
beauty of the mellow soil.

"Here he is!" they would shout at the sight of him.
"Here he is! Here is Mahlon stretched out on the
ground! Look at him there! What a fool he makes of
himself!"

"What do you want?" he asked them.

"Mahlon, we came to take you to the city tonight,"
they would say. "There will be music and dancing,
much to eat and much to drink, and pretty girls to talk
to all the time. Get up from there and come on to the
city and have a good time with us tonight."

"Why should I go to the city and dance and sing when
I am happy here? Why should I go there to eat and
drink? Why should I go there to talk to pretty girls
when I am happy where I am?"

"But, Mahlon, you fool, you have none of those things
here," they would say. "You can't dance and sing with
only yourself. There are no pretty girls here to talk to."

"Yes, but I am content where I am. I would much
rather stay here and be content."

"You are a fool, Mahlon," they would say to him. "Get up off the ground and stand up like a man. Why do you lie there with your fingers dug down into the soil? You are a fool, Mahlon! Get up off the ground!"

"I love the earth. I am most content and happy when I am close to it. I do not wish to get up. I want to stay where I am."

"Did you hear what Mahlon said? He said he loved the earth! He tries to make love to the ground! He lies there upon it as though he were a girl's lover! What a fool Mahlon is! He pretends that the ground is a girl and that he is her lover! Get up, Mahlon, you fool!"

They went away laughing. When they had passed out of sight, he got up and found his sack of seed and pressed them one by one into the mellow soil. The earth closed over his fingers, caressing his hands tenderly. He got down on his hands and knees and breathed deeply of the sweet perfume of the earth.

The rains came and the sun was warm and the seed swelled and sprouted. Soon the whole field was covered with the tall plants that rustled in the breeze.

And still the people came. They would not leave him alone. They came after dark, saying to themselves that Mahlon would be in his house then and that he would not leave and go into the fields when they began talking.

They knocked on his door and went inside.

34

"Now, Mahlon, you have planted the seed and the corn has grown in your fields. We want you to sit still and listen to us."

"What is there to say to me now?" he asked.

"Mahlon, you are growing old. You must stop being a fool and listen to us. We are your friends."

"What do you want to say to me?"

"We have taken pity on you, Mahlon. We have brought a woman with us, and she is waiting at the door for word to come inside. She is alone in the world, too, and she will make you a good wife. Both of you will find contentment together. Will you let her come into your house, Mahlon?"

"No," he told them. "I am content as I am."

"Stop being a fool, Mahlon!" they said. "A great lover of the earth like you — a man who goes out and lies on the earth as though the earth were a girl — should have the wisdom to let the woman come into the house and be with you."

"If you were as content as I am, you would not be here now trying to bring misery into my life. You want me to give up my happiness because you have none."

Leaving them, Mahlon went out the back door and walked across the fields. He found his way through the darkness until he was far from the lighted windows of his house and then he got down on his hands and knees.

Beneath him was the warmth of the earth and the soft-
ness of the mellow soil. He lay down upon it, stretching
out his arms and legs and pushing his hands into the
earth. After that he lay silently through the night with
his face pressed upon the ground while his heart beat
painfully against it.

A Message for Genevieve

EXACTLY ONE year ago tonight was the last time I saw you.

I opened the door and went out into the hall without looking at you again. My cigarettes were forgotten on the table under your shaded lamp, but I did not think of them then. You closed the door behind me and locked it. The key turned the lock and fell on the floor. You ran back, picked it up, and thrust it into the keyhole with trembling fingers.

After that you ran across the room and fell on the bed and cried. I heard the sound of your falling upon the bed, and I heard your first sobs as you began to cry. I will never know what you did after that, because I walked down the hall to the stairway and ran down to the street. The elevator was not running at that time of night. The elevator was never running after midnight, was it, Genevieve?

I left the building and walked out into the street. Out

there it was snowing again. The snow that had melted during the afternoon had left a sheet of grayish gleaming water that had frozen on the pavement during the evening. There was ice everywhere underfoot. I fell twice before I could reach the corner. Once I slipped backward, my feet flying upward in front of me; the next time I fell forward and landed heavily on my chest. The man at the newsstand on the corner laughed when he saw me fall. But he was always laughing at something. Do you remember the afternoon when we ran to the corner and got there just as the bus was leaving? We ran down the street trying to catch it, but it was going too fast. He laughed at us then because we had missed the bus and would have to wait half an hour for the next one. There was another time, too, when he laughed at us. That was the evening when we tried to pick up the quarter he had glued to the pavement. You remember that, don't you, Genevieve? We were on our way to that little restaurant near the park. That was the evening we stayed there until after midnight listening to the bearded violinist play Slav folk music. Maybe you remember the musician's name. I've forgotten now.

It has been a year, Genevieve, since I last saw you. You told me to go. You said I had to leave. It was between two and three in the morning. We had been in your room since four o'clock that afternoon. I wanted to stay longer, and you said you wanted me to stay. But you were afraid. You said I had to leave. That was all. That was the end. I left.

It is easy to say that now, Genevieve, but it was not like that then. We had discovered something greater than the love we had known before. If it had been the love we knew, and were so familiar with then, and nothing more, there never would have been anything to make you frightened. But it was something far greater than the love we had known. We knew of affection and desire and ecstasy, but we knew nothing of such a strange new magic. We tried to talk about it, but there were no words to explain its meaning. And you — your body trembling and your voice speechless — were so frightened by our discovery that you were afraid to let it reveal itself to us.

There was good reason for what you did. You were trying to guard our love against a mysterious enemy. We had been in love with each other for a long time, Genevieve, and you were afraid to let anything else take its place. You withheld your consent for me to explore the unknown, and you were afraid to undertake it alone. It would have been necessary for one of us to lead the way — to take the other by the hand on such an unknown journey. But you were afraid of what might be revealed. You were jealous of our love and you were afraid to turn it free, even momentarily, while we explored the darkness.

That was a year ago tonight. I left you, Genevieve, and went out into the street. The snow was falling gently and without hurry. It had been snowing all evening while we were together, and when I went out into the street, there were deep drifts of new white snow as far away as I could see. The sidewalk had been scraped, and the ice gleamed on the pavement. I fell twice before I could reach the corner and get on a bus.

Now, I am far from you, Genevieve. I am a thousand miles away. Does it seem strange to you for us to be so far apart? It seems strange and unreal to me. A year ago I was with you. Six months ago I was wandering aimlessly from place to place — I do not even remember the names of the places I went. All that time I was trying to escape from the memory of you. And now, after all those months, I can at last sit here and seek the memory of you.

It is a pitch-black night outside, and a log fire is flaming in the fireplace. The logs pop and crackle, and sparks spew like fireworks as they swirl up the chimney into the dark night. Outside it is raining in sheets of wind-blown water, and I am alone.

Alone, except for Dan. Dan is with me, just as he has been since the first day of his life and just as he will be until the end of his days. He is stretched out beside me, sound asleep in the warmth of the fire. Every once in a while he growls in his dream and barks savagely. He caught a rabbit yesterday. I heard him barking in the field for nearly an hour before he succeeded in catching it. When he had finished eating it, he came back and tried to tell me what he had done. After that, tired and exhausted, he stretched out in front of the fire, his four muddy paws on the warm hearth, and went to sleep.

You remember Dan, don't you, Genevieve? Of course you do. All those times when the three of us went walking in the woods could never be forgotten. You used to stop and scratch Dan's ears, and he would look up at you and try to tell you how much he liked for you to do that, and you would talk to him as though he were a person. Dan remembers you, Genevieve. Whenever I show him some of the things you gave me, he recognizes your scent at once; he wags his tail and barks as if he never wants to stop. Dan remembers you, even though it has been a whole year since he last saw you.

I hope it is snowing now where you are. That's the way I want to remember winter a year ago. Do you remember that afternoon before we went to your room? The snow was dry and clean, and when we walked through the park, the crunching-sound under our feet propelled us on and on until we both were so tired we

could not go any farther. Just as it was beginning to
grow dark, we turned around and walked back through
the park and over the frozen lake to your room. We
warmed our hands when we got there, and then I kissed
you.

Genevieve, I loved you. I tried to tell you how
much I loved you, but I could say so little. You remember that, don't you, Genevieve? I stopped trying to tell
you after that, and there was silence for a long time.
You said you understood.

We were standing at the window, and you were fac-
ing me with a tilt of your head. You were always like
that when we were alone together, Genevieve; I don't
know why, but it was one of your ways.

We left the window and went to the other side of the
room. I tried again to tell you how much I loved you, but
there was so little I could say. You smiled understand-
ingly, and then you pressed your hand over my mouth,
and pretended that you had not heard even the few
words that had reached your ears. You knew it was useless to try to say things with words, too.

After you had sat down on your bed, you drew me
to you and pressed my face against your breasts and
stroked my head with the tender touch of your hands
and I did not try to say anything more. It would have
been useless. Nothing mattered then except the feel of

your warm body in my arms. You must have known why I did not try to say anything after that, because you did not speak either. After a while I got up and tilted the lampshade so the light would not shine in your eyes. When I came back to you, I began kissing you.

That evening in your room was the most memorable time of my life, Genevieve. We lay together for hour after hour, and then just after midnight you got up and brought me a glass of water. After that you came back again into my arms.

It was between two and three o'clock in the morning when you sent me away. I opened the door and went down the hall and then down the stairway to the street. As I left, you were crying because you had told me to leave. I could hear you crying when I reached the far end of the hall, but as I went down the stairway to the street the sound faded away and I never heard it again. And all the time I was repeating to myself what you had told me. You said I had to leave because you could never give any man your complete love.

Ever since that night when you told me to leave, Genevieve, I have been thinking of you. Most of the time I was wondering when I would see you again. But now I have begun to know that I will never see you again, Genevieve. After a year, and a thousand miles away, I can talk like that. Now I can understand what you meant when you said you could never give me, or any man, your complete love. You were afraid it would not be enough for your own satisfaction.

We will never be together again, Genevieve. Yesterday I could not have said that, but now after a whole year I can. The year has passed, and now it is too late to go backward in time.

I am sorry, Genevieve — not for me, not for you; I am sorry for us. Without your fear of complete love, we could have been happy together until death, and now it is too late. Can you hear me, Genevieve?

When another man comes to you and tries to tell you that he loves you, let him say it. And when he tells you that he loves you, and if you love him, do anything but send him away. Let him stay and drive away your fear. Don't let happen again what happened to us. Even be fools together, Genevieve, when the time comes, but do not send him away as you did me. If you will let a man love you in his own way, you will never again feel that you have to seek satisfaction with another woman.

Sylvia

D<small>EAR</small> S<small>IR</small>:
   I understand from reliable sources that you are acquainted with a great many people in the State of Iowa, and I am writing you this letter because I do not know of any other means of getting in touch with Sylvia's relatives. They will recognize her if they hear about this letter, and I hope you will speak about it to as many people as you can. I would send this directly to one of her relatives if I knew any of them by name.

   I am an American myself, but I cannot sign my true name, because it would endanger me in my present work.

   When the war got under way in Europe, all the foreign newspaper correspondents in the capital were moved into the Majestic Hotel by the government and told they would remain there for the duration. All the regularly assigned German, British, Italian, and French correspondents had been called home and those who remained were Americans, Japanese, and Scandinavians.

Sylvia moved into the Majestic Hotel, too.

She had come over three years before that on a month's assignment for an American women's fashion magazine. At the end of her first week here she resigned her job by cable and settled down at the Grand Hotel, where many of the correspondents were living at the time.

Sylvia was a very happy girl from that moment on. She loved the life the correspondents lived, and everybody who knew her agreed that she was worth her weight in gold. She had learned almost overnight what kind of news was wanted, and it was a seller's market.

Her habits became as regular as clockwork. Every afternoon she would disappear during the cocktail hour, and nobody would see her again until the next morning at eleven, when she would walk into the Majestic breakfast room. Every correspondent in the capital would be at the big round table by the windows waiting for her with pad and pencil.

They used to joke with Sylvia a lot when she came in, telling her that if she had something really good she ought to look out for herself and query the *Times*. Sylvia always laughed and said that she would rather sell her story to the *Republic*, because it had more prestige in the profession. Then the correspondents would joke some more and bid for exclusive rights for the *Henepen News* and other such names they would make up. After all the joking was over, they would settle down and take notes on what she had to tell them. After that all the correspondents would hurry up to their rooms and type out their cables. At the end of every week they handed her a thick envelope containing her remuneration.

None of the correspondents ever checked on Sylvia's information after the first month, because by that time they knew for a certainty that she had never given them a single word of false information. Besides, there was no way of checking up on most of her information, because where she obtained it was as much of a secret as the means she used in obtaining it.

All the correspondents liked Sylvia, and every time they had an opportunity they would ask her about herself. Where she came from, what her real name was, and all sorts of questions like that. They never learned much about her, although she did tell them that she had been fired from every newspaper in Chicago and New York for carelessness, inaccuracy, tardiness, and so on.

I never knew how much of what Sylvia told them was true, because I always had the feeling that while Sylvia never uttered a false word when it came to news

and information, she never made a single true statement
about herself or her personal life.

But sitting at the Majestic bar, or in the breakfast
room, she was the queen of journalism. Every important item of news that had leaked through censorship
during the past six months had first been reported by her
to the correspondents. Where she obtained the information, or how, and by what means, and from whom, were
unanswerable questions. There was no doubt in anybody's mind that Sylvia maintained an exclusive and
privileged pipeline to sources that no correspondent had
succeeded in reaching. During all that time everybody
admitted that if it had not been for Sylvia, all the news
of any journalistic value would never have appeared in
print in America or elsewhere.

All had gone well for six or seven months. Then, one
morning at five o'clock, the military marched through
the street past the Majestic Hotel with Sylvia — taking
her to court-martial.

At five-thirty she was condemned, at five-forty-five
she was blindfolded, and at six she was executed inside
the walls of the military prison.

None of the correspondents knew for several hours
what had happened. When Sylvia failed to appear in the
Majestic breakfast room at eleven as usual, the correspondents became worried, but they felt certain she

would come in before much longer. They sat around the big table by the windows drinking coffee and brandy until long after noon. Then somebody phoned the police and inquired about her. The police refused to give any information whatsoever, but referred the call to the military. That was how the correspondents learned of Sylvia's execution. It was a terrible shock to everybody.

All the American correspondents cabled the story to their offices, but, because nobody knew Sylvia's last name, none of the New York papers ran a single line of the story. The wire service editors in New York likewise killed the story, and that is why no newspaper in Iowa received a dispatch. When the correspondents asked the editors in New York why the story was not used, the editors cabled back that they could not use such a story because no American would be court-martialed and executed abroad without some sort of exchange of notes between the governments. The editors had queried the government in Washington, and they were told that such a story must be without foundation of truth because the embassy staff in Europe refused to confirm that the executed girl was an American.

Several months later one of the American correspondents accidentally found a clue. He was in one of the government buildings one morning when he overheard a conversation in which Sylvia was mentioned. He went back to the Majestic Hotel and told the other correspondents. They all got busy and began checking their sources of information. Little by little the trail led back to the government building where the correspondent had first overheard the mention of Sylvia's name.

The correspondents worked at the mystery for several weeks before they found enough evidence to convince them that Sylvia had been employed as a spy for one of the warring governments. Just the same, they were convinced that the information Sylvia had been bringing to them was accurate to the comma. She had made her news-gathering for the correspondents so accurate and reliable that they were not able to find anything misleading. That was when they realized that she had made news-gathering a blind for her other work. The other work was her real job, because she had been trusted by the other warring government to obtain all its important military information, which was then secretly transmitted abroad by some other paid spy.

The correspondents did not stop at that, however. They continued investigating until they found evidence to prove that Sylvia was an American by birth, and that she had renounced her American citizenship during her first week there in order to become a spy. It was agreed by all who knew her that her only reason for doing such a thing was because she craved excitement and was impelled by something in her past life to live dangerously.

There is a little town in the southern tier of counties in Iowa where almost everybody will remember Sylvia, even if that is not her real name. She was the daughter of a well-known doctor who still practices medicine there, and I think her mother is still alive, too.

In case her relatives would not recognize Sylvia by the name she took, they will when I mention the fact that about six or seven years ago she ran away from home and roamed the Middle West and the Mississippi Valley with a notorious bank robber and killer. Both of them had their pictures in newspapers all over the country for several months while the police were looking for them. Then, after nearly a year, the man she was with was killed in a chase with the police in a small town in Missouri, and Sylvia dropped out of sight. She was never seen again in Missouri, or anywhere in the Middle West. That was because she left the country, escaping into Mexico, and finally made her way to Europe. During that time she changed her name several times, the final one she used being Sylvia. Even if her relatives do not recognize her by that name, they will certainly know now why they will never hear from her again.

In my present work I cannot make myself known, but sometime I want to come to Iowa and tell Sylvia's relatives, especially her mother and father, if they are still living then, where Sylvia was buried, and other such matters that might interest them.

Naturally, I cannot sign my true name to this letter, and it would be senseless to sign a fictitious one. However, when my work is finished, I will gladly reveal my name, if it will be of any interest then.

Yours sincerely,

An American Abroad

AMERICAN SKETCHES

The Barber of the Northwest

A NORTHERN PACIFIC freight train rolled in from the prairie, eighty-eight cars long, and ground to a screeching stop on the embankment above the baseball park. The visiting House of David team, bearded to a man, was beating the local team 7 to 5 in the seventh inning, but the Bismarck team was up with two men on, one out, and the lead-off batter was planting a single in right field. A relief pitcher climbed out of the House of David dugout and began warming up on the sideline. It looked pretty bad for the visitors.

The N.P. freight shook itself two or three times from engine to caboose, like a dog remembering his fleas, and half a dozen hobos clambered out of the gondolas and box cars and dropped to the ground. The six or seven men and boys who remained on the train would reach Fargo sometime that night.

Down in the grassy dell the fifty-cent fans were on their feet in grandstand and bleachers. The Bismarck batter had driven a long fly to center field for a sacifice hit, and a runner scored.

A man who had jumped from one of the gondolas sat down beside me on the edge of the embankment and began opening a leather satchel.

"What's the score?" he asked, taking some things from his satchel and placing them in a neat row on the ground.

I pointed to the scoreboard down in the dell.

The man with the satchel glanced up for the first time and squinted down into the playing field.

"Whiskers, eh?" he said, laughing a little to himself. "Never had a shave in their lives."

The bearded House of David team was making an easy out at first base and leaving the field for its turn at bat. The score stood 7 to 6 in their favor now.

The man beside me closed the satchel and pushed it aside. Picking up a whetstone with one hand, he reached with his other hand for a pearl-handled razor, selecting it from a collection of three. Then he began honing the blade.

"Barber?" he asked.

"Who? Me?" I said.

He nodded solemnly.

"No," I told him.

He took a quick, close look at my face.

"I can give you a once-over in a couple of minutes," he offered.

I felt my face.

"Thanks, but I guess I can get by till tomorrow," I told him.

"O.K.," he said.

The man with the razor poured a little water from a tin canteen into a cup and began working up a lather. When it was ready, he set up a mirror and began applying it to his face.

"Do you happen to be a barber?" I asked him.

He stopped what he was doing and looked at me.

"Don't you know me?" he asked in surprise.

I shook my head.

"Haven't you ever traveled on the N.P.?"

I told him I never had.

"O.K.," he said, leaning forward to look into the mirror. "I'm Happy Flynn. I've been riding the N.P. for three years. Everybody who rides the N.P. knows me. I'm the barber."

"A barber on the freights?"

"Sure," Flynn said. "On the freights."

A big Negro swung off the refrigerator car behind us and stretched out on the grassy embankment. Stuffing his pack under his head, he lay there watching the baseball game in the dell.

The barber got up, halfway through shaving, and went over to where the Negro lay. They talked for a few minutes, and then he came back. He sat down in front of the propped-up mirror and applied fresh lather to his left cheek.

"Holes in his pockets," Flynn said.

"Broke?" I asked.

"Not even a dime for a once-over," he said, scraping his chin.

"What's the cost of a haircut?"

"A quarter and up — up when they've got it."

"That's cheap enough," I agreed.

"Cheap is right for a good trim by a graduate of the Kansas City Barber College. So, O.K. A guy has to work cheap and fast to make a living these days. O.K."

The House of David team scored two runs on bunched hits off the Bismarck pitcher. The Negro sat up.

"Just look at those ball-playing fools!" he shouted. "They're good enough to be right up there in the big-time league!"

Flynn wiped his razor and felt his face. He was looking down into the dell.

"Whiskers, eh? Every last son-of-a-gun of them. Even the batboy has got fuzz on his face, I'll bet."

The engine whistle tooted like a foghorn. Half a dozen men got up from the grassy embankment and

stretched. A rumble ran through the string of freight cars as the engineer took up the slack in the couplings. A moment later the wheels began turning eastward.

Several men swung up the sides of the gondolas and box cars. The Negro and the barber, with their backs to the train, were watching the pitcher fan a Bismarck batter.

"Going East?" I asked Flynn as the train gathered speed.

"East or West, it's all the same to me," he said, shaking his head. "I can get my living either way between the Lakes and the Rockies. As soon as that ball game is over, I'll take the next freight — whichever way it's going."

"Can you save any money?" the Negro asked him.

"Save money? Sure, I save money. I save more barbering on the N.P. than I did working in the Palmolive Building in Chicago. Sure, I save. Why wouldn't I? I don't have expenses. I've got it planted all the way from St. Paul to Spokane. If I get short, all I have to do is drop off and pick up a few dollars. O.K."

The train was passing at an increasingly rapid rate of speed. The faces of the men standing upright in coal gondolas, lying on flats, and sitting with their legs dangling from box car doors, were flashing past faster than they could be counted.

"Don't you have a family to take care of?" the Negro asked Flynn.

"None for three years," he answered. "I had to drop my family when I took to the N.P. My wife couldn't see the N.P."

The freight was making so much noise that nobody said anything more until the caboose had passed. Flynn turned around and watched the train disappear down the track. There was a grim smile on his face, and he rubbed his eyes several times before he looked in our direction again.

"Did you hear what I said?" he asked us. "I was saying that my wife couldn't see the N.P. My kids could, though. They could see the N.P. That's the only thing I feel sorry about — those kids of mine. They wanted to go railroading just as much as I did."

After Eighty Years

THE GRAY-BEARDED old man shuffled out of the wooden-fronted rooming house and made his way to the curb. For several minutes he fumbled with the torn opening in his coat, trying to extract from it a small package wrapped in tough brown paper. The men on the corner watched him disinterestedly.

A man with a gray hat tilted on the back of his head hurried past. Half a dozen steps away he stopped and called back.

"Hello there, Cap!"

His attention distracted, the old man's fingers moved from the torn pocket to the top of his head. He scratched at the mat of gray hair under the bedraggled brown cap. Before he could reach the man in the gray hat, the man turned around and walked away.

Cap moved unsteadily across the pavement and bumped into the wall of the rooming house. Then once more he shuffled back to the curb as quickly as he could.

The package in the lining of his coat again drew his whole attention. Then all at once Cap jerked, tugged, and twisted the coat lining and the package, at the same time swearing in a husky roar. The men on the corner turned and watched him.

"Hello, Cap!" one of the men said. "What are you mad about today?"

For a moment the old man's hands wavered between the package and the top of his head. Finally, he dropped the twisted lining and raised both hands to his cap. He quickly jerked it off and scratched his head with both hands, at the same time swearing hoarsely at the wooden building. One of the men in the group came closer.

"Why do you keep on living in that fleabag, Cap?"

Cap stopped and glared at him.

"Because it's home to me, that's why. Don't you know what home means to a man?"

"They've got better homes than that for old men like you. Get wise to yourself, Cap. I hate to see you living like that. All you have to do is go to the relief office and they'll find a decent place for you to live. Then you'll really have something to call home."

"I've taken care of myself for eighty years, and I can keep on doing it, too. And I didn't ask you to butt in with your advice, neither."

"Look here, Cap," the other man said. "Listen to reason. There's no sense in old-timers like you bumming nickels and dimes on the street. Things have changed, and you ought to change with the times. Get wise to yourself, Cap, and go on over to the relief office like I told you. They'll fix you up. You're too old to be out on the street panhandling like you do."

The old man replaced the cap on his head and once more began trying to extract the package from his coat. He was swearing hoarsely again.

"To hell with you, Cap!" the other man said, walking away. "Nobody can tell him nothing! If he wants to beg all day for a few dimes, let him keep it up till he drops dead. And if you ask me, the sooner he drops dead the better off he'll be."

Cap, with a final twist, pulled the package from his coat. It came out torn and rumpled. Ripping off the paper, he took out a roll of bread and began munching on it with tender gums. The brown paper fluttered away in the breeze.

After the roll had been eaten, Cap wiped his hands on his coat and shuffled toward the corner. The group of men backed away as he moved closer.

"Help an old man," he said in a singsong voice, the words sounding feeble and faint as they trickled through his gray beard. "Help an old man. No hard feelings if you ain't got it to spare. Just a nickel or dime or anything. Help an old man."

Nobody in the group said anything. They just stood there and watched him as they did every morning when he left the rooming house with his roll of bread and began his day's begging. This time his pants and coat appeared to be more worn and ragged than ever before, and his feeble singsong voice was almost inaudible.

Cap's thin earth-colored hand, palm upward, was thrust closer to the men as though he could barely see what he was doing.

"Help an old man," he repeated. "No hard feelings if you ain't got it to spare. Just a nickel or dime or anything. Help an old man."

Somebody took a wad of chewing gum out of his mouth and dropped it into Cap's hand. Cap's fingers closed over the sticky gum. He felt the gum in his hand for a moment, and then he began swearing hoarsely through his tobacco-stained gray beard as he wiped his hand on his coat and pants.

"Beat it, Cap," one of the men said. "Get away from here. If you don't have enough sense to stop begging on the street and let the relief office take care of you, you

ought to crawl off and die somewhere. Now, stay away from this corner after this."

Cap shuffled away toward the next corner, holding out his thin earth-colored hand, palm upward.

"Help an old man," he said to nobody in particular. "No hard feelings if you ain't got it to spare. Just a nickel or dime or anything. Help an old man."

Grandpa in the Bathtub

SOME PEOPLE SAID it had not rained a jugful in all Kansas that year, but Grandpa Price had caught ten gallons of rainwater that had fallen in Nemaha County since New Year's Day. Of course, what little rain that did fall was not enough to mature the corn, keep the pastures green, and water the stock; but Grandpa Price had put tubs and pans under the eaves of the house and barn during three showers, and he had saved the water to show for it. He kept the water in bottles and jugs, every one of which was well corked so that not a single drop would leak out or evaporate.

In August, during the worst of the drought, Grandpa brought out his stored water and said he was going to take a bath. He carried the water upstairs to the bathroom and was soon sitting as naked as a plucked jaybird on the side of the tub.

Fanny, his daughter-in-law, had dinner all cooked and ready to serve, and the children were standing at the kitchen door begging to know when they could eat. Fanny went upstairs and knocked on the bathroom door. Grandpa Price yelled for her to come in if she wished to, and she opened the door just enough to speak to him and to see what he was doing.

"It's dinnertime, Grandpa, and the children are begging for their meal," she said. "Please hurry up and come downstairs so we can eat."

Grandpa Price splashed his feet in the water, kicking it all over the room. The walls and floor were dripping wet.

"Look at the water, Fanny!" he shouted, splashing some of it on her face. "Did you ever see so much water in all your life?"

She closed the door and ran downstairs.

"Go tell your father to hurry to the house, Henry," she told the oldest boy. "Something dreadful has happened to Grandpa."

Henry ran down to the barn, where his father was still working. He had to pass Grandpa Price's crib of corn on the way, and he stopped and pushed his fingers through the wire netting and got a few kernels off a cob. He popped the corn into his mouth and began crunching it between his teeth. Grandpa had said he would thrash anybody, boy or woman, who was caught taking as much as one grain of corn out of the crib, because he was saving it to plant when there was favorable moisture in the ground. The hundred bushels of seed corn had been brought down from South Dakota by Grandpa Price when he moved in to live with his son Dale and his family.

When Dale got to the house, he asked Fanny what the trouble was upstairs in the bathroom. She told him about Grandpa Price sitting on the side of the tub and splashing water all over the walls.

"Let's eat dinner before we try to get him out," Dale said. "Maybe by then he'll be ready to come out of his own accord."

After dinner was over Grandpa Price was still upstairs, sitting with his feet in the water. He had been up there nearly three hours already.

The three boys went down to the corncrib and worked a few more kernels through the wire netting. As long as Grandpa was in the bathroom, they were not afraid of being caught eating his seed corn.

The corn was six years old and, although his son and daughter-in-law had tried to persuade him to let some of it be planted before it was too old to germinate, the key to the crib still had not been turned in the padlock since the day it was brought down from South Dakota. Every time the corn was mentioned, Grandpa said he was saving it for the lean years. He had lived in

the Dakotas for twenty years, and he said he had not lived there for nothing. The lean years were still ahead, he told them.

When Fanny went upstairs at suppertime that evening, Grandpa Price's bedroom door was open and she could see that not a piece of furniture was left in it. The bed and dresser were missing, and even the chairs were gone. She ran to the bathroom and opened the door.

Grandpa Price was still in the bathroom, and the furniture had been stacked in the small room until there was left only space for the tub. Grandpa was sitting, naked, on the edge of it and splashing water with his toes.

"I've never seen so much water since I left the Dakotas," he told Fanny.

Fanny was about to shut the door and run downstairs to tell Dale what Grandpa Price had done with his furniture when he reached out and caught her arm. Still holding her, he reached behind him and brought out a padlock key. It was the brass key to the corncrib door.

"Here, Fanny," he said, thrusting it into her hand. "You take care of my corn for me while I'm up here, but I want you to dole it out sparingly. Now that we've got plenty of water, the time's come to use the seed corn. I know I can trust you not to be wasting of it."

Fanny took the key and backed out of the bathroom

before Grandpa could change his mind about the corn.

Downstairs, Fanny ran to Dale and told him what Grandpa Price had said, at the same time giving him the key. They had seen the shiny brass key before, and there was no mistake about its being the key to the hundred bushels of Dakota corn.

Dale took the key and started to the corncrib. At the door he stopped, listening to the splashing of water upstairs in the bathroom.

"It's a good thing we had those three little showers this year, after all," he said, smiling at Fanny. "They didn't make enough water to sprout grass, but it was enough to make Grandpa think the lean years are behind us. I'm going to plant some of that corn and make it grow even if I have to haul water for it all the way down from the Dakotas."

The Man Under the Mountain

FOR ELEVEN YEARS now I have known the man under the mountain. I have visited with him and talked to him about once every six months during the past decade. I have no idea how long he had been under the mountain before I saw him the first time, and even he is not certain how long it has been.

But the name of the man under the mountain is Dan Caster, and some people say Dan Caster has been under the mountain as long as there have been red hills in Alabama.

"How long have you been down there, Dan?" I asked him the last time I talked to him.

"Quit asking questions and help me get out of here," he said.

"I don't know how to get you out," I told him.

"I got put here, didn't I?" he said. "Well, then there ought to be a way to get me out."

Dan Caster is the kind of man who, under different

circumstances, would be known as a solid citizen. Solid, that is, as a good credit risk, as a man of his word, and as a hard-working family man. But that is not the way it is now. Down there under the mountain, Dan is kicking, squirming, shouting his lungs out. He is down there under a massive mound of rock and earth which rises half a mile above the surrounding countryside.

Less than a hundred miles away, on top of another mountain, men have set up the massive figure of a Vulcan who was released from the red ore of the Alabama earth and cast into the form of a heroic statue. The Vulcan of Alabama is silent; he was made that way.

Dan Caster, the man under the mountain, was made with the power of speech. He learned at an early age how to express his needs, wishes, and convictions with the common words of American life. He went to work early in life as a farmer; he married; he was the father of seven children. During all that period in life he was talking a little. He would say he wanted to buy a new tool for farming; he would say he wished to send all his children to school for the best education they could get; he would say he believed it was wrong for his landlord to weigh, gin, and sell the cotton he had grown without permitting him to see the figures.

Dan talked that way for eight or ten years — nothing wholly unbecoming in a tenant, but perhaps a little too loud in the presence of the cotton buyers when his landlord was listening to every word he said.

"You'd better watch your talk, Dan," the landlord told him. "If you don't watch out, you'll talk yourself out of house and home."

"I'm only talking about what's right and what's wrong," Dan said. "I raised the cotton, and I ought to see the figures."

"It's my land the cotton was raised on," the landlord said.

"But it was my sweat that did it," Dan told him.

That was how it happened. The landlord moved Dan and his family off the bale-to-the-acre land to a back part of the farm where the land was soil-washed and eroded. Back there Dan had a difficult time of it trying his best to raise a quarter of a bale of cotton on eighth-to-an-acre land.

After several years of raising short crops, Dan Caster said he wanted better land to farm. The landlord told Dan to get off the farm; he even went so far as to bring a deputy sheriff to see to it that Dan and his family got off the farm before the sun set that same day.

Dan moved away. He found a shack of two rooms for his wife and children. There was no land to cultivate, and so he started out to look for abandoned pine stumps. He had an axe and it was his plan to split the fat pine, tie it into small bundles, and sell it for kindling to people in town. The trouble was that people had no use for the fat pine kindling, and nobody bought it. Then the landlord came along and told Dan that he was going to hound him for the rest of his natural and supernatural life for chopping up the pine stumps.

"Those old stumps had been dumped in the ditch beside the public road," Dan protested. "They didn't belong to anybody."

"They grew on my land to start with," the landlord said, "and that makes them more mine than yours. And just for that, I'm going to teach you a lesson."

The next thing Dan Caster knew, he found himself half a mile deep in the mountain. He tried to dig his way out, but the hard stone cut his fingers to the bone. He kicked with his feet with all his might, only to feel the impregnable stone that entombed him. After that he shouted, he yelled, he cried out with all the force of his lungs; and all the good it did him was to make him realize that nobody could hear him.

That was when I came along the first time and tried to help Dan Caster get out. When I found out that I could not accomplish anything alone, I tried to get others to help me. Everybody I talked to had a lot to say about Dan Caster and whether it was right or

wrong for him to be where he was, but nobody offered to help.

"I've got my own self to look after," one man said. "I can't spare the time."

"If he'd minded his own business and kept his mouth shut to begin with, he wouldn't be where he is," another man said. "And that's what I'm going to do. Mind my own business and keep my mouth shut."

Several years passed and the time came to raise the massive Vulcan on the mountain a hundred miles away, and I once more began talking to people about digging Dan Caster out of his mountain. Everybody shook his head. Some said it would be an impossible task; some said it was not worth the trouble; others said it was somebody else's job, not theirs.

After that I went to the landlord and asked him to help get Dan Caster out. But the landlord said he had Dan Caster where he wanted him, and, if anything, he would do his utmost to keep him there.

Finally, I went to Dan's friends and neighbors and asked their help. All of them were sympathetic, and all of them felt sorry for Dan's wife and children; but, they said, things being as they were, it was not a wise move for them to make. They said they were afraid they might wake up some day and find themselves under the mountain, too.

Dan Caster is still under the mountain — deep under the mountain. Unless you go there and place your ear on the ground you cannot hear him shouting down under all that earth and stone. For a man buried so deeply, he makes a lot of noise, though. With your ear pressed tight to the side of the mountain, you sometimes hear him so plainly you will think the rumbling vibrations might be an earthquake.

In fact, when houses shake and the earth rumbles, people living miles away will say it is not an earthquake, but only Dan Caster, the man under the mountain, clamoring to get out.

A Short Sleep in Louisiana

JIM WORTH and his wife sat down and ate their breakfast of finger-thick slices of bacon, deep-pan cornbread, and coffee after waiting nearly half an hour. The sun was more than an hour high by that time, and the bacon and bread had got cold. It had been at least ten years since Jim Worth was as mad as he was that morning.

"Maybe the poor old man is sick and can't move," Jim's wife said timidly, being careful not to make him any more angry than he already was. "He didn't look any too well when he came to the door last night and begged for a place to sleep."

Jim swung his arms over the table, knocking over his cup of coffee. His wife set things straight and poured fresh coffee into his cup.

"I asked him an hour ago if he was sick and needed a doctor," Jim said. "He told me he felt as good as he ever had in his whole life."

"But I heard him say you could send for the doctor if you'd pay for the visit," his wife said.

"That's proof enough he ain't sick," Jim shouted at her. "When a man's sick enough to die, he'll say he'll pay his own doctor's bills."

Jim's wife sank back into her chair. She was careful not to make him any more angry than he was already, and she prayed under her breath that he would not get into a violent mood this time. As it was, she was fearful that he would take it into his head to do something harmful.

When Jim Worth finished eating, he got up and went to the back door. Then, stepping to the ground, he looked through the open window into the bedroom where the old man was wrapped in a blanket and sprawled comfortably on the bed.

"You're the last human that'll ever beg a night's sleep out of me," Jim shouted through the window. "A man my age ought to know better than let a no-account tramp inside the house, anyway. I don't give a hoot in hell if you are eighty years old — or even ninety years old. I wouldn't let you inside my house another time if you got to be a hundred and eighty years old and came begging on crutches for a place to sleep."

Jim Worth had got up in the morning before sunrise ever since he was old enough to remember. When he married his wife, Sophie, she had begged him to let her sleep at least until the sun had risen, but Jim had made it clear that anybody who slept in his house was going to be up and dressed before the sun reached the horizon.

The night before, Jim had let Sophie talk him into letting the old man sleep in the extra bed. It had been a cold damp night outside. It had been drizzling rain since morning, and when night came, the rain settled down to a steady fall. The old man had been struggling through the sticky Louisiana gumbo all day, and he appeared to be on the verge of falling to the ground at any moment. Jim said at the time that he had never seen a more pitiful old man in all his life.

The old man had said his name was Humphrey Fallon, and that he had no home and no known relatives. He said he had been tramping the road through one state after another for the past forty years.

Jim stood at the window and looked at the old man in the bed.

"That bed tick has got insects in it," Jim shouted through the window.

"What kind of insects?" Humphrey Fallon asked, lifting his head from the pillow.

"Bugs and lice, to name some," Jim told him, at the same time wondering what Sophie would say if she had heard him. "Once they get on you, you'll never get rid of them. They'll plague you the rest of your life."

"Maybe so, but they haven't bothered me yet," Fallon said. "I'll stay till they do."

Jim went to the barn and carried out a long scantling. He took it to the window and poked and jabbed at the old man several times.

Fallon rose up in bed enough to look at Jim Worth through the window.

"Durn if you ain't the most anti-hospitable creature I ever ran into," Fallon shouted at him.

"You get out of my bed," Jim said.

"I'll get out when I finish my rest and sleep," Fallon told Jim. He lay down again and pulled the blanket under his chin. "For all I care, it might just as well be night as day. When I want to rest and sleep, I don't care which it is. Now, leave me alone. I'll get up when I'm good and ready."

Jim went to the back yard and got the mosquito smudge-pot. Then he filled it with pine lighters and set it afire. When the smoke began boiling upward, he carried it to the bedroom window and put it inside on the floor. Presently the room began to fill with black smoke, and Fallon sat up to see what was happening. In a few moments he began coughing.

"You folks here are the most anti-hospitable on the face of the earth," he shouted at Jim. "I always had a

good respect for Louisiana folks till I ran into you."

It looked for a while as if the smudge-pot would drive Humphrey Fallon out of the bedroom. However, he lay down again and spread the blanket over his face. After the smoke had filtered through the blanket, it was not strong enough to affect his breathing.

Presently Fallon sat up in bed and looked at Jim.

"I've been living in this world for eighty years, but I've never had such a short sleep in my life before," he said. "What time is it, anyhow?"

"It's past time for you to get out of my house."

"You ought to be ashamed of yourself to treat strangers so anti-hospitable," he told Jim. "You'll suffer for it, though, somehow or other."

Jim went to the barn and got an armful of straw. He piled the straw against the side of the house and set fire to it. As soon as Sophie saw what was happening, she ran out of the kitchen with a bucket of water and tried to throw it on the fire. Jim grabbed her and held her with all his might. She began screaming and yelling, and after a moment Fallon came to the window.

"Now you'll get out of my house!" Jim shouted at him. "You'll get out, or be roasted alive!"

"You folks in Louisiana are just plain damn fools," Fallon said. "Anti-hospitable ain't nowhere near the right word for you."

He stood at the window watching the flames and smoke against the side of the house.

"Maybe you don't know it," he said to Jim, "but I'm just as hard-headed as they come. Don't be surprised if I stay right where I am."

"Maybe you're going to stand there and let the house burn down, but I'm not," Sophie told Jim. She ran to the pump and got a bucketful of water. After several trips to the pump the fire gradually was stopped.

Going to the window, Jim looked inside to see if Fallon had left the room. Instead, he saw Fallon getting back into bed and pulling the blanket over his head. Before going to sleep, he sat up and looked at Jim standing at the window.

"If I don't get the rest of my sleep now," Fallon said, "the next time I come this way I'll go through Arkansas and not put foot in Louisiana. Besides, I've heard that the folks up there ain't nearly so anti-hospitable as you folks down here."

A Country That Moves

TWENTY MILES from the Mississippi River, on the Missouri side, Frank Hanley was frying hamburgers in his roadside lunch stand and listening to what was going on in the country. He said he learned more about what was happening here, there, and everywhere by listening to what travelers told him than by reading the newspapers.

Frank told about a man stopping for a hamburger and a cup of coffee a few days before and telling him that the New York Yankees would win the World Series that year. He said the year before a man had told him the same thing and he had not believed it. Frank said you can see for yourself what happened last year. The Yankees did win it, just like the man said.

"That proves you can learn more by listening to travelers than any other way," Frank told the man at the counter. "Since the country started to move on

wheels, everything has changed. Even the radio and
television can't keep up with things, no more than
newspapers can. That's because nobody settles down
long enough to hold a steady job any more. Everybody
gets on wheels and travels."

The man at the lunch counter, between bites, asked
Frank why that was.

"Because it's just like the eighteenth century, that's
why," Frank said.

"Is the eighteenth century something I ought to know
about?" the customer asked.

"Don't you remember reading in history at school
about how people in those days used to be on the road
all the time? The inns were full, all over England and
Europe, and people traveled day and night. There were
good people on the move, like religious folks, and there
were bad people, like highwaymen who would kill a
man for a farthing."

"Uh-huh," the customer said, chewing a bite of hamburger.

"And another thing I just learned," Frank said, "is
that the Detroit Tigers are going to have a chance at the
World Series next year."

The man at the counter put down his cup and pointed
at the steaming coffee urn. Frank filled it up.

100

"That's anybody's guess, about the Detroit Tigers," the man said.

"Maybe so," Frank told him. "But the fellow who told me that was the catcher, and he ought to know."

"What catcher?"

"The Tigers' catcher," Frank said. "That's how I get reliable facts and information."

Frank then told him about a family that had stopped at the lunch stand just the day before for some hamburgers. He said they had been on the road a year and a half already, and were still traveling.

"If you had any idea of the traveling that people do these days, you'd know how I find out so much," Frank said. "Travelers crisscross this country like rat tracks under a corncrib. It's exactly like the eighteenth century."

"That's a funny thing you keep on saying about the eighteenth century," the other man said. "I'd never even heard about the eighteenth century before."

"That's what comes of getting your education over the radio and out of newspapers. Neither one of them ever mentions the eighteenth century, because they don't know about it either. And that's why I'm an educated man. I stand here and listen to travelers tell all about the country and learn what's happening one place and another. And then when I close up at night, I read history."

The man at the counter wiped his hands on the paper napkin and called for a pack of cigarettes.

"That's a lot of foolishness," he told Frank. "You can't believe everything you hear. And if you do believe it, you get fooled more times than not. I wouldn't even believe what you said about the eighteenth century."

"I'm not like you," Frank said. "I've learned what to believe. People zipping up to Chicago, down to New Orleans, over to New York, across the country to Los Angeles, everywhere there's a crossroads, day and night, rain and shine — that keeps the country on the move and the tales fresh and reliable. If one man tells me a tale about something that happened in Texas, I can check up on the truth of it before the day is over by asking the next man from Texas who stops for a hamburger. In the eighteenth century tales got pretty wild because there was no way to check up on them like I can."

The man blew smoke across the counter. "I don't want to hear anything more about the eighteenth century. I'm talking about here and now."

"All right," Frank said, "I'll prove to you how I get the true facts. Just yesterday a man from Alabama was here and he told me about a petition some men in a work

camp got signed up and sent to Washington. They sat around the camp with a lot of time on their hands, specially on rainy days, and so they petitioned the government to furnish them with a revival preacher. The government had been handing out free tickets to moving pictures, and those fellows said they wanted to listen to revival preaching for a change."

The man at the counter laughed. "I'd believe what that was you said about the eighteenth century quicker than I'd believe that tale. Anyway, since you probably heard about the petition before the government had time to get it, I don't guess you know yet if they're still getting free movie tickets or preaching."

"I can answer that," Frank said. "Whether the government got the petition before or after I heard about it, a revival preacher moved into the work camp and settled down to preaching. Now they have preaching every night and all day Sunday."

The other man, shaking his head to himself, paid for the hamburgers and coffee. He put on his hat and walked toward the door.

"That's what's wrong with the country now," he said to Frank. "People like you flood the country with tales like that, and the rest of the people have got so they won't even believe their own grandmother any more."

"There's nothing wrong with the country," Frank

said angrily. "It's a fine country. This country's all right. The wrong thing about it is people like you in it who don't know the difference between the eighteenth century and the eighteenth hole on a golf course."

CZECHOSLOVAKIAN
SKETCHES

Bread in Uzok

Y OU BEGIN to think you are going to the end of
the world when you get ready to go to Uzok, but
when you reach the village, you know at once it is not
the end, because you find that on top of the mountain
a few kilometers away Poland begins. Up there on the
crest of the Carpathian Mountains, in an open field,
there was a place where a line had been drawn across a
path, and on either side of the line were soldiers with
fixed bayonets on their rifles, staring at each other all
day and all night.

But back in Uzhorod, which is something of an out-
post of civilization itself, everyone gave the appearance
of thinking that Uzok was actually the end of the world.
Uzok is not the easternmost town in Carpathian Ruthenia,
because that is Jasina; but it is the northernmost town in
the province, and when you see the people of Uzok for
the first time, you understand why some think it is the
end.

The taxi driver in Uzhorod had been to Uzok before, and once was enough as far as he was concerned. He said he had not been able to sleep for three nights after he had been to Uzok. Rather than go there again, he made a counter-offer. He would tell us about Uzok and that would save us the trouble of going there. By that time a good-sized crowd had collected around us in the street, and we urged the taxi driver to count up the kronen for the distance once more. It came to a fairly large sum of money, and he then decided it was worth it after all. He asked us to excuse him for five minutes.

When he came back, he brought his pistol and an extra box of cartridges. But in addition to that, he brought five loaves of black bread. The Ruthenian hotel owner, who had been in the crowd a few minutes before, brought three loaves of bread and handed them to us in the manner of a man wishing you well on a canoe trip around the world. Behind him a moment later came the Czech policeman who had stood on the curb and listened to our debate with the taxi driver. He handed us a bundle containing two loaves of bread. Suddenly caught up in a kind of blind excitement ourselves, but far from knowing why, we went into a store and bought an armful of bread. The Jewish storekeeper presented us with three additional loaves when we paid for the ones we had bought. When we asked him why he gave us bread we did not pay for, he simply said because we were going to Uzok.

Several times during the trip we asked the driver why we were taking so much bread to Uzok and, furthermore, why the hotel owner, the policeman, and the storekeeper had given us bread to take there. His only reply was to the effect that we would best find out for ourselves when we got to Uzok.

The village of Uzok opened up suddenly, as it should have, from a curve in the road. It was a thing of beauty.

There were two rows of white-walled, dark-thatched houses, one row on each side of the winding road, extending for about two kilometers. Behind the houses the bare fields sloped upward for several hundred meters until they met the wide blankets of snow halfway up the sides of the mountains. Above the snow the bright green pine and spruce forests began. Due north on top of the highest range was the Polish frontier.

It was in the late spring, and the fields and houses were wet with melting snow.

We stopped at the side of the brook. By then we were already in the village, and on each side of the road the houses stood barely more than an arm's length apart. Three or four children were playing in the icy water where they had built a dam across the brook. There was no one working in the fields, no one working around the houses. Not more than one dwelling out of six had smoke in the chimney.

Then, a few moments later, doors began opening one after another on each side of the road. Children were the first to come out, being bolder; men came next, and finally the women. Before we could get back to the automobile, thirty-five or forty persons had gathered there.

The taxi driver, who said again that he had been to Uzok before, knew exactly what to do under the circumstances. He backed against the trunk on the rear end of the car, shifted his pistol to his coat pocket, and ordered the people to stand away at a distance. Already there was pushing and shoving and shouting. The driver had a heavy stick as long as his arm, which he waved in front of him while he fumbled nervously with the trunk lock behind his back. Within a few minutes after we had reached Uzok, a crowd of fifty persons or more had collected and begun begging for bread. But that was not all. More people were coming as fast as they could run. We knew then why we had brought bread to Uzok.

The trunk, in which the bread was stored, was opened, and the driver reached inside. The crowd began to push and shove. A moment later, when the people caught sight of the loaf in the driver's hand, there was a sudden surge forward. The driver tossed the bread back into the trunk, shut the top, and struck at the people with his stick, threatening at the same time to take out his pistol if they did not stay back. They went backward several steps, but shouted louder than ever.

The first loaf was chopped in half with the big butcher knife we had brought with us, and the first piece was given to an old man. He turned and pushed his way out of the crowd, pulling a six-year-old boy with him. He did not look back even once. On the way to his house he held the half-loaf of bread in both hands, talking excitedly to the boy as a father to his son. The man was telling the boy that they were going into the house to eat the bread, and that they would not eat it all at once in a hurry, but would chew it slowly, a bite at a time, so it would last longer. They went into the brown-thatched house, still not looking back, and closed the door and bolted it.

The people around the car were begging for a piece of bread. Some of them asked for only a small slice if they could not have as much as half a loaf. Old women pleaded for just a bite, if no more. There were tears in the eyes of some who got down on their knees and asked if they could only have a little of it.

When about half of the bread had been given away,

the driver shut the trunk and locked it. He still held one whole loaf under his arm. Scarcely a third of the people there had had any of the bread.

The last loaf was chopped in two, one piece handed to a small girl, and the other piece given to one of the old women. The woman, with tears flowing from her eyes, thanked God for the gift. She stood there staring blindly at us, her hands trembling so much that she had to hug the bread in her arms against her chest to keep from dropping it.

"It has been seven years since I tasted bread," she said brokenly. "Seven years since I have known the taste of bread in my mouth."

"I wish we had more to give you," the driver told her. "But there is so little to divide among so many people."

"I don't want any more than this," she said, sobbing and stroking the crust. "I just wanted to taste bread once more before I die, and now I can."

"Why haven't you had bread in all this time?" she was asked.

"The prince, who comes from Hungary, does not want anybody on his land any more, because he said human beings scare away the wild boars he keeps there to hunt."

"Are all his peasants as hungry as you are?"

"There are five or six hundred who are hungry. The prince is angry because he thinks the state is going to take his land from him and give it to us. He said he would never give us work and food again as long as this is a part of Czechoslovakia."

"There are fields behind these houses. You should have a right to use them to keep from starving. You could raise grain there, couldn't you?"

"There is no wheat in my house to sow the fields," she said. "Seven years ago when we were hungry we ate the wheat. There are oats, a little, but oats won't make bread. I grind the oats and cook it with water, and that is all. It is not bread. It is only oats."

The woman bent her head as if in prayer and caressed the chunk of black bread with trembling fingers. Turning away, she passed through the crowd that made way for her and shuffled slowly toward her house. It was a house like all the others, with a dark brown-thatched roof, almost black, and it had whitewashed plaster walls over a kind of adobe brick. The walls of the house were no higher than the woman's head, and she had to stoop a little when she walked under the eave to the door. The high-pitched roof was nearly three times the height of the walls, and the building looked like a small white stone under a thick clump of almost black grass. She entered the door, closed and bolted it behind her.

Although about half the bread had been given away, the people who stood there expectantly did not ask for the loaves that were left. Even those who had seen the bread in the trunk, and had smelled of it, but who had not received any, did not utter any protest. They stood in silence around the mud-splashed automobile looking at us. When we told them we were leaving, they still did not say anything. And when we drove away, some of them tried to follow by running up the road behind us, but after we had gone half a kilometer they turned back.

We asked the driver why he did not give away all the bread, and he said there were other people at the far end of the village who were even more hungry, and that they should have what was left. We began to protest that it did not matter to whom the bread was given, but that the important thing was to give it away as quickly as possible. The driver, shaking his head, said he had been to Uzok before, and that he would not dare go to the other end of the village without bread.

We drove slowly up the winding road between the two rows of same-looking houses. There were many children playing in groups along the brook, but the older people remained out of sight in their houses.

The village began to appear poorer and poorer. The

houses were no different in size, shape, or condition, but the groups of children were larger and more poorly dressed.

When we stopped the second time, we had already passed the center of the village. There were only two stores there, and neither was large. The driver said that people who did not have bread to eat did not have money to spend in a store.

Children again were the first to come to the automobile when we stopped. Several of them knew the odor of bread, and they began crowding around the trunk at the rear end of the car. The grown people were not so quick to come out of their houses as they had been at the first place we stopped in Uzok. They were cautious and more suspicious, and took care to find out if we were friends or tax collectors.

The driver, with stick and pistol, went to the trunk and unlocked it quickly before a crowd had gathered. He quickly chopped several loaves in half and handed the pieces to the children. They grabbed the pieces of bread like starving dogs snatching a bite of food, and dashed wildly toward their homes, afraid the bread would be taken from them if they remained in the road.

By then the people in the houses had seen the bread, and they began coming madly toward us. The driver was ready. He shut the trunk, shouted at the people to stand back, and threatened them with the stick and pistol. He held them back while he reached into the trunk and took out the bread.

The first man to get a piece tucked it against his belly like a football and ran into his house as though his life depended upon it. In his haste he did not close and bolt the door. When he got inside, he handed the bread to the older of the two women there. She was his mother. His wife stared at the piece of black bread with eyes that almost burst from her head.

The children crowded around their grandmother, begging and pleading for some of the bread. The man and his wife looked on as if in a daze while the grandmother cut the bread into small pieces about the size of a thumb.

There were twelve children to feed. There were also the man and his wife, and the grandfather and grandmother. The sixteen persons filled the one room of the house until there was barely space for another person to enter. Under one of the beds was a young sow and a litter of six pigs. The sow grunted complainingly, and the little pigs squealed hungrily at the flabby teats.

After the bread had been cut into many small pieces, each child was given one. After that all except the grandmother took a piece and chewed it strangely and slowly. The old woman shook her head and refused to take any.

"After nine years without the taste of bread in my mouth, I am afraid," she said.

No one urged her to take it, but she picked up one piece that might have been hers and gave it to her husband. The old man looked up into her face but did not say anything. He took the bread she gave him, holding for a short moment the thin hand that had touched his. His eyes were so filled with tears that he could not see where she went when she turned away. None of them saw her when she opened the rear door and went noiselessly out of the house.

The driver had given away all the bread. Several men and children went to the trunk of the car and looked inside when he held it open in order to convince them that there was no more bread left. Those who had not received any stood silently in the road, looking at us and the car.

They did not ask us if we were coming back to Uzok again bringing bread. They seemed to understand that it probably would be a long time before anyone came there again, except perhaps the tax collectors. They had learned that it was best not to look forward to such things.

The people stood there watching us forlornly, their

tattered gray homespun trousers and coats appearing even more worn and shabby than they had when we first got there an hour or two before.

"Thank you," somebody in the crowd said. "God bless you."

The driver put away the pistol which he had carried but never used, threw away the stick, now that it was no longer needed, and swept up the few crumbs of black bread in the bottom of the trunk. Reaching down, he pinched the remaining crumbs between thumb and forefinger. Before he could throw the crumbs away, half a dozen hands were thrust at him, and once more we heard the voices begging for bread.

The driver placed the crumbs in one of the outstretched hands and closed the trunk. The faces around us relaxed into deep, gaunt-looking lines. The voices were silent. The men, women, and children whose eyes stared at us knew that it would be a long time until there was bread again in Uzok.

Wine of Surany

IT WAS A hot summer day with waves of warm winds blowing little puffs of dust over the dry fields. We drove along the lane toward the cluster of farm buildings on a knoll half a kilometer away. On one side a man was driving a team of oxen yoked to a plow which broke the land into furrows that looked like ripples on a millpond. The tall poplar trees grew in a stately row on each side of the lane. Their branches were long and green, and it was cool there. The dust in the shaded lane was still damp with dew.

We drove up to the large, rambling, one-story house and stopped. We sat in the car for a while and waited. There was no one to be seen about the house. The piazzas were screened and vine-clad, and there was a summer stillness everywhere. In the garden there were roses and a large round table surrounded by chairs. There were newspapers and stacks of magazines and several books on the table.

While we sat in the automobile waiting for someone to appear, we heard a drone of voices off in the distance. The drone was low-pitched and insistent. We got out and walked in the direction from which the sound came. It was away from the house, and it led us through a grove of tall oak trees to a small cliff. The knoll on which the buildings sat ended abruptly at the edge of the grove. There was a sharp incline there, and down below us we could see the flat land of Southern Slovakia. The fields were divided into squares like city blocks and were separated from one another by hedges and rows of poplar trees.

Immediately below the cliff were the slopes of vineyards, and below them were fields of grain and paprika.

The young vineyard directly in front of us was being hoed and weeded by groups of Slovak girls and women. They worked in straight lines of twenty-five or thirty each, and walking up and down in front of each line were two or three Hungarian overseers.

The overseers kept up a steady flow of advice, praise, and abuse. Their monotone voices floated over the vineyard in layers of dust stirred up by the girls and women. While we stood there, one of the overseers used his stick on the knuckles of one of the women who had fallen several steps behind the line. While she was striving to catch up with the others, he cursed and abused her for her slowness.

Some of the women sang, some talked, and some made no sound at all. The overseers walked up and down in front of them, swinging their sticks and urging the women to hoe faster and destroy the grass and weeds cleaner. Occasionally one of the women worked a step ahead of the line, and even then the voice of the over-seer was sharp and abusive, even in praise.

While we were standing there watching the men and women on the slope below, a tall, bareheaded man came out of the house and called to us. He was wearing tan trousers and shirt, and his face and arms were strong and brown.

We walked to meet him, and told him why we had come. He was pleased that visitors had come to see his vineyards. He said he was very proud of his vineyards, and that they were the finest in all the country surround-ing Surany.

"Let us sit down at this table," he said, pointing into the garden. "It is much more pleasant here in the shady garden than in the vineyards at this time of day. But I should tell you the truth. I am selfish. I want you to sit here in my garden where I can entertain guests to the best of my ability."

After we had sat down, he called to a servant and ordered wine from the cellar and asparagus from the kitchen.

While we were waiting, his wife came from the house and sat down at the table.

"Wine?" she asked her husband.

"I have ordered wine and asparagus," he said proudly. "Our guests from America must taste our wine and asparagus. We must give them the best."

"This is the proudest day of my life," she said to her husband. "I never thought we would have guests from America. It has never happened to us before."

The man and his wife looked at us and smiled. We understood little that was said. He and his wife were Czechs, and they spoke neither English nor French. We leaned forward and listened closely while he spoke slowly and distinctly to enable us to hear each sound. Every once in a while we grasped the meaning of some Czech words, and then waited hopefully for others that we might understand. Only in that way were we able to follow what was being said.

The wine came, and later the asparagus. The wine was 1930 vintage, and the asparagus had been taken from beds only that morning. He was proud of them both.

"My wife and I come from Bohemia," he said. "We

came down here to Surany many years ago and bought
this land. Bohemia is hard and cold, especially in winter.
Slovakia is soft and warm, almost the whole year
around. We like it here. We would never go back to
Bohemia, unless —"

His wife leaned forward quickly and put her hand
on his arm. They looked at each other solemnly for a
long time. Presently he leaned back in his chair and
laughed.

"Let's not spoil the visit of our American guests by
thinking of the dark side of life," he said. "We are proud
to be visited by American guests. It has never happened
before in our lives. It will never happen again."

"Why could it never happen again?" we asked.

"It would be too much of a good fortune to happen
again," he said quickly.

The wine bottle was empty, and the servant was sent
for more.

"Wait!" he called to the servant. "This time bring the
1929. It is for our guests."

His wife smiled happily as she nodded to us.

"It is a great honor to have guests from America,"
she said. "The wine must be the best."

We ate the asparagus hungrily. The huge stems were
long and bleached, and they were served with little pots
of melted butter.

"I hope you do not have such asparagus in America," he said, speaking slowly and distinctly, "because we want to welcome you to Southern Slovakia by giving you something you do not have in America."

"It is much better than we have in America," we told him. "Even the best is not as good as this, and sometimes it is so tough we have to cut it with a knife and fork."

"A knife and fork!" he exclaimed, looking at his wife.

Both of them leaned back in their chairs and laughed loudly. All of us joined in.

"More wine!" his wife said after that.

"The better the wine, the faster it goes!" he said.

He sent for another bottle.

"This time bring the 1928," he told the servant.

Shadows began to fall across the garden and table, and the sun was not so hot as it had been earlier. The drone of voices from the young vineyards on the slopes grew louder as the day's work drew near the end. The overseers were striving to urge the girls and women into a final burst of speed and industry.

New dishes of asparagus and hot butter were brought, and the wine was poured.

"Why did you come to be our guests?" the man asked.

"It was accidental," we told him. "We left Surany

this morning and were driving through the country, and when we saw your fields and vineyards, we decided we would like to stop. That is our only excuse."

The man and his wife smiled with pleased expressions. A moment later he leaned forward and spoke earnestly.

"Now that you are here, you must not leave. You must stay and be our guests for a long, long time."

His wife nodded approvingly.

"It is too good to be true," she said. "We want you to stay. It has never happened to us before."

After so much wine, it was becoming more difficult all the time to understand much of what was being said. And each new bottle of wine disappeared faster than the previous one.

The servant was sent for another bottle. The next one was to be 1927 vintage.

"Soon we are going to reach the treasure of them all," he said. "Soon we will be tasting 1925. That was the year of our first grape harvest in Surany. There are only a few bottles of that year left. I have saved them for the wedding of our oldest daughter. But no longer will I save them. I have other daughters to be married, and I may never have guests from America again."

His wife nodded approvingly. Then she got up and left us for several minutes. She went into the house, and when she came back, she whispered excitedly to her husband. All at once both of them burst into laughter.

"It is the grandmother," he told us, still laughing. "The grandmother is so funny."

They continued laughing until the bottle of wine was empty. The servant was sent to the cellar for the 1926 bottle.

When the wine was brought and poured, the man leaned forward and told us that the grandmother in the house had threatened to leave. He said she was packing her clothes and saying she was going back to Bohemia.

"Why?" we asked.

They leaned over the table and spoke carefully.

"Spies," they said. "She thinks you are spies."

All of us laughed.

"She thinks you are spies!" he said in a loud voice. "German, Hungarian, French, Russian, American — she's not sure which. But spies just the same. She says she is going back to Bohemia, where she will be safe from spies. She says Bohemia is the only safe place left in the world."

It was becoming more and more difficult to understand what was being said, and we were not sure that the Czech and his wife understood a word of what we were saying.

"Tell her we are American tourists — not spies," we

tried to say clearly and distinctly. "Don't let her get upset. She might actually start out walking to Bohemia."

He shook his head bewilderedly as he poured more
wine. The servant was waiting to be sent for more.

We could see the grandmother at the windows occasionally. She parted the curtains, peeped out at us, and
then closed them hastily.

The girls and women from the vineyards were coming through the grove on their way home from work.
They were tired and work-stained as they came with
lagging feet past the garden. When they were directly in
front of the garden, as though obeying an order, they
suddenly burst into song. Their faces were tired and
haggard as they stood there singing until the song was
finished. There was a sharp word from the overseer, and
they turned and walked homeward in silence, relieved
that they would not have to stay any longer and sing
for the landlord and his guests.

"Slovak workers, Hungarian overseers, and Czech
landlords," the man said sadly as he watched the girls
and women pass from sight. "And over us all, the
German God Almighty."

No one said anything for a while after that. The long
shadows covered the garden and house. The sun was
setting in a red glow over the vineyards.

"Nobody is free," he said finally. "Slovaks answering

to Hungarians, Hungarians answering to Czechs, and Czechs answering to the German God Almighty."

His wife sent the servant for the 1925 wine.

"It could be worse," he said slowly. "It could be much worse. Anyway, we are free today — us Czechs. Tomorrow we will not be free."

The wine came and was set before us. The bottle was dusty and old, and the numerals 1925 could barely be read in the faded, hand-lettered ink.

"But this is no time to be sad and solemn," he said. "We are entertaining guests from America. It may never happen to us again as long as we live. We should not be sad and solemn."

After the bottle of 1925 wine, we got up to leave. The man and his wife tried to get us to stay for the night, for the rest of the week, for the remainder of the year. They hurriedly sent the servant for the last bottle of 1925 wine in the cellar.

"Slovak, Hungarian, Czech, and the German God Almighty," he said. "We all answer to the German God Almighty."

His wife hurried into the house for several moments. She soon came running back to the garden. The grandmother had left. She had pinned a farewell note on her pillow: *Those foreigners are spies and they are here to find information to give to the enemy. I am going back to Bohemia, where I will be safe from spies.*

The man and his wife read the note again. They looked at each other, shaking their heads bewilderedly. Then suddenly his wife ran down the lane to overtake the grandmother and bring her back.

The man watched his wife until she had reached the grandmother, and then he came back to the table and shook hands with us. He spoke rapidly in Czech, but he soon realized that we could not understand what he was saying. He put his arms over our shoulders and drew us against him while tears ran down his cheeks.

We attempted to apologize for being the cause of the grandmother's running away, but we all gave up when we realized how hopeless it was to try to talk in unfamiliar words. He seemed to understand the way we felt, though, and he gripped our hands in both of his. Tears continued to fill his eyes.

"It does not matter," he said slowly as he looked at us. "It is not your fault. She was only doing what my wife and I know in our hearts we should do. After so much wine, I can tell the truth. All of us should go back to Bohemia and live and die like good Czechs. The Hungarians want my land, even though it really belongs to the Slovaks. If the Hungarians take it, the Slovaks will become their serfs instead of mine. And while all of us wait to find out who is master and who is serf, the German God Almighty is coming to be the master of us all."

He stood with bowed head while we got into our car and drove off into the twilight. When we looked back for the last time, he was disappearing in the darkness of night that was falling all around.

The Dogs of Ceske Budejovice

IN THE EARLY autumn the sun shone brightly in the deepest streets of Ceske Budejovice at seven o'clock in the morning. Warm breezes blew through the cobblestone streets from the rich flat countryside, and the air was sweet with the odors of ripe fruit and drying wheat. A light mist that had settled over the city during the night had disappeared when the sun rose, but the air was still moist and clinging.

It was warm then after the cool night, and there were people standing on their doorsteps and hurrying through the streets hatless and coatless. In the north, in the Giant Mountains, there were frost on the meadows and snow flurries in the forests, but in the south there was warmth like that of midsummer. Summer always lasted longer in Ceske Budejovice than anywhere else in Bohemia.

In the park a city gardener was cutting grass with a lawn mower. He stopped and wiped his face.

"It would be a wonderful thing if the world stayed just as it is," he said dejectedly. "But it won't, though. It will change. The grass will stop growing, and the leaves will fall. I worked all spring and summer caring for this lawn in the park and making it beautiful for people to see, and now in a little while it will turn brown and curl up and die, and all the care I took of it will be for nothing. I am sad, because I think of it a lot."

Several large work dogs trotted down the street, keeping close to the sides of the buildings where the shade was coolest, and stopping occasionally to sniff familiar odors as all dogs will. In a vacant lot across the street a group of children played with a football, and some of them were shirtless and barefoot. A woman on her way to the market raised a parasol over her head.

"It is true," the gardener said. "I am sad today. It is the way I feel inside. It cannot be helped." He pushed the lawn mower into the grass and walked away in the clatter of the machine. All the other words he said were lost in the noise the mower made.

The dogs that had trotted down the street a little while before were coming back again. They were making their early morning rounds of visits as they did each day. At the corner, the pack divided. Some of the dogs continued up the street out of sight, and the others turned into a narrow alley.

The Dogs of Ceske Budejovice

Soon in every street there were large thick-coated Alsatians and great shaggy-haired Saint Bernards. All of them were cross-bred and strong. They had to be strong, because they were the work dogs of Ceske Budejovice.

The sturdy dogs worked in single harness and in double harness, pulling carts of wood and coal, cement and lumber, over the cobbled streets from seven in the morning until seven at night.

Most of the dogs had already been harnessed for work that morning, but there were still many that ran up and down the streets barking and panting. Others lay in the shade beside their carts waiting to be called if their masters found work for the day.

The owner of a large brown-and-white Saint Bernard sat on the doorstep of the house where he lived and watched his dog wrestle playfully with a gingerbread-colored Alsatian in the street. He held the dog's harness across his knees.

Every once in a while the Saint Bernard stopped playing and trotted inquiringly to his master. He licked his master's hand and waited patiently for some word from him. The man said nothing, but shook his head, and the dog turned and trotted back into the street where the Alsatian waited.

After that the two dogs barked, growled playfully,

and approached each other in a circular movement, one advancing clockwise and the other counterclockwise. They went around in circles several times and then suddenly, as if by prearrangement, they sprang simultaneously, meeting chest-on in mid-air, and locked their forelegs around each other and rolled over and over on the ground. They wrestled and bit and rolled until they both were tired, and then one relaxed and lay still, and then the other one did likewise. After several moments they got to their feet, shook their coats from head to tail, and the Saint Bernard trotted once more to his master on the doorstep. The Alsatian waited in the street.

The Saint Bernard came wagging his tail and panting. The man shook his head again. The dog looked up into his face for a while, and then he licked his master's hand and went back into the street to play some more.

"I always have hope," the man said. "It may be that I'll have a task to do today. Somebody yet may want to hire my dog and cart to carry some coal or lumber. It is still morning. It is not yet too late in the day to get a task to do."

He gazed into the street where his dog was again wrestling and rolling with the Alsatian. The sun was getting higher all the time, and when he turned and looked at the shadow on the sidewalk that was like a sundial, he began to be worried about getting a job to do that day.

Most of the other men who lived on the same street had left home with their dogs-and-carts, and they were already at work. One of them had loaded his cart early, and he came up the street pulling the strap beside his dog.

"There are so many of us," the man on the step said. "There are so very many, and there is not always enough work for all. It would be better if there were not so many dogs-and-carts in Ceske Budejovice, but it is our only way of earning a living. Just the same, if there were fewer of us, then there would surely be horses and motor trucks, and then none of us could find work to do with our dogs. It is best the way it is. It would be very bad if there was no work for us. A little is better than none."

The neighbor with the loaded cart passed out of sight up the street.

"It is early yet," the man on the doorstep said, nodding to himself. "It is still not eight o'clock. There is almost the whole morning yet to come."

He stared at the shadow on the sidewalk as if he thought it possible to stop it from moving until he had found a job of carting. He rubbed the harness between his fingers while his eyes were staring at the shadow.

"I had a day's task, not yesterday, but the day before," he said. He looked into the street where the two dogs played. "But there are no tasks to be hired for once the morning is over. It makes me feel sad not to have a task to do. My dog has to go hungry then."

He stroked the leather harness with his broad muscular hands.

"Those who speak both Czech and German get more tasks to do than a man like me who speaks only Czech," he said. "The Germans do not give me tasks because I cannot speak like they do. They pretend not to understand me when I speak in my own language. It is a pity I do not speak German, but I have not learned, and now I am too old."

He glanced quickly at the shadow on the sidewalk. The sun was rising rapidly over the street.

"There are not many Germans in Ceske Budejovice," he said — "not anywhere near as many as there are in some other cities in the north. But there are some, and that is enough sometimes to mean the difference between having a carting job and not having one."

Occasionally a work dog trotted through the street, but those that came that way did not stop to play with the Alsatian and Saint Bernard. The dogs that were allowed to run free did not stay away from home long at a time. After going on short trips through the streets, they always returned to their masters to find out if there was any work waiting for them.

At the far end of the street was the large park where the gardener was mowing the grass, and across from that were the railway yards. Coal from the north was unloaded there. Householders and shopkeepers came down the street from the city square when they wanted to bargain for a dog-and-cart to carry coal to their doors, and sometimes they went all the way to the railway yards before hiring a cart at the price they wanted to pay. The people bought their coal in small lots, and usually two or three loads at a time were all they would bargain for.

At that time of the year, when many people were buying coal in order to have it on hand when the first winter weather came, there were many loads to be carried, and almost every dog-and-cart owner in the city was able to get a share of the work.

The poorer people, though, could not afford to buy coal, and they were the ones who bought wood for heating and cooking. It was such a long trip to the forest and back, and the pay was so small, that not many men wanted to overwork their dogs by carting wood when there was a chance to get a job carrying coal.

"It is hard on the strongest dog to cart wood from the forest," the man said. "It is almost seven kilometers there, and as many back again, and the wood is green and heavy. I have seen many fine dogs break their strength coming back from the forest pulling a cart loaded with green heavy wood. One can make only two trips a day there and back, and the pay is only a few kronen. If the dog has his strength broken, there are not many men rich enough to buy another one. I could not buy another dog myself. I am not rich enough."

A woman who lived in one of the houses nearby came up the street pulling the strap beside her cart dog. She had left home before seven that morning, because she had been hired the day before to cart a load. There were several large boxes in the cart, and the load was a heavy one, but she was singing as she came up the street beside her dog. She had loaded the boxes in the railway yards, and she was taking them to a shop in the city square nearly two kilometers away. Her dog was a sturdy-looking cross-bred Alsatian. He was friendly-faced, and tall and brown.

"It is good to see a widow working," the man on the step said. "It is good to see that a widow can find tasks to do. I do not envy her. I am glad she has found a task that will pay her money. She is a widow."

The cart rumbled over the cobblestones and went out of sight up the street. The two dogs had played so much that they were tired, and they lay on their fore-legs resting and panting.

"My dog is growing old," the Saint Bernard's master said. He rubbed the leather harness between the palms of his hands until it glistened in the sunshine as though it had just been cleaned with soap and polished. "My dog has been a good animal, and a faithful one. He has never strayed away from home in all the years I have owned him, and he has always been eager to take the harness. When he grows too old to work any longer, I will be sad."

He sat and thought about his dog, remembering the many times when there was nothing to feed him, and how the dog worked hard just the same because he seemed to understand they were earning a few kronen with which to buy food.

"I will be very sad when that time comes," he said after a while. "I am a poor person, and I cannot afford to feed the old dog and a young one, too. I may not even be able to buy a young one. But if I do buy a young one, I cannot feed them both. It is not possible for me, an old man, to earn enough kronen to feed two animals. I go without food myself sometimes even now so my dog can be fed. It would not be possible to earn enough to feed all three of us. The pay for a task is small, sometimes only two or three kronen, and there are many days — like today —"

He stopped suddenly when he realized what he had said, and looked at the shadow on the sidewalk. There was scarcely any shadow left at all. The sun was already mid-morning high in the sky.

"There are many days when I do not have a single task to do," he said, shaking his head. "And feeding two dogs —"

"Couldn't you find somebody who would take care of your dog when he grows old?" we asked him. "He is still strong-looking, and he will be able to work a long time yet. By the time he grows too old to work, couldn't you find somebody who would care for him and feed him?"

"That could not be done," he stated firmly. "In Ceske Budejovice, a dog must earn his own living while he can work, and after that only his master takes care of him. It is the life we live, and nothing changes it. I have heard of nobody who would care for a stranger's dog when his days are done and he is too old to work. When I was a young man, I cared for my dogs as long as they lived. Now I am old, and I cannot do that any longer."

He got up from the steps and went into the house without saying anything more. It was as if he could not bear to think of the future. His dog came to the step,

stood there waiting for a while, and then he stretched out to rest on the sidewalk until his master called him. The sturdy Alsatian sat on his haunches watching the Saint Bernard for a while, and then he got up and walked to his own doorstep across the street and lay down upon it.

We left the street and walked toward the railway yards. When we got there, we could see six or eight dogs-and-carts being loaded with coal. When one was loaded, the owner took the strap over his shoulder, and then he and his dog got the heavy cart started. Together, side by side, they pulled it up the cobbled street toward the city square.

It was late in the morning when we left the street and went into the park again. The gardener was still mowing the grass. He stopped when he saw us, and waited until we reached him.

"Soon the grass will die and there will be no more to cut," he said sorrowfully. "I am very sad. I do not like to talk about it. All I want to do now is hurry and finish cutting it for the last time. Then I'll go home and wait for spring to come so I can care for it and make it beautiful again."

Leaving the park, we went up the street where we had sat on the doorstep earlier that morning. The brown-and-white Saint Bernard had been harnessed to his cart, and he was sitting on his haunches and watching the door of the butcher shop on the corner. Presently the door of the butcher shop opened, and the dog's master came out with several pieces of meat on a paper. He laid the meat at the dog's feet and stood back to watch him. The dog ate the meat in a few quick gulps, and after it was all gone he licked the paper to make sure he had left none.

"Only a little while ago I found a task to do," the man said, rubbing the dog's head and ears, "but first I had to feed him."

The dog finished licking the butcher's paper and shook his coat from head to tail. When his master, smiling, looked down and patted him again, the dog licked his hand.

"I did not have any food to give him this morning, and I could not spend the last kronen I had until I found a task to do." Man and dog were looking at each other. "It hurts me when he has to go hungry."

He led the dog-and-cart down the street toward the railway yards, where coal from the north was being unloaded. The dog strained eagerly at his traces, his long bushy tail waving like a plume as he trotted in order to keep pace with his master. After that they were soon out of sight in the railway yards.

WHEN YOU THINK OF ME

When You Think of Me

THE MOIST SPRING earth flowed past the vestibule window like a broad flooding river.

Ted Burton, swaying on the narrow platform of the railway coach, waited impatiently for the train to slow down for the station. His tanned face was tense with excitement as he took another draw on his cigarette and pressed his flushed forehead against the cool pane of glass. His mouth twitched nervously as he watched the warm flat land unfold before his eyes. He could see every pool of glistening rainwater in the freshly plowed fields, every flowering fruit tree, every green bush in the hedgerows; but nevertheless, it was difficult for him to believe that at last he was actually coming back home from war.

The Negro porter was bringing his baggage to the vestibule door.

"How close are we to Ridgeway now?" Ted asked for the third time that morning.

"It ain't far," the porter said, glancing out the window. "There's that big cornfield out there now — where it looks like they raise nearly all the corn in the world. When we pass that, Ridgeway's sure to be dead ahead. Is Ridgeway where you live, Corporal?"

"You bet it is!" Ted said. He watched the cornfield for a moment. "I wonder if the town has changed much since I've been gone —"

"No, sir! It ain't changed. Ain't nothing in this country changed much. It's been just like it is now ever since I can remember, and it'll stay that way, too. I sure would hate to live in this country and see it change either way, good or bad. It just wouldn't be the same place if that ever happened."

"I guess you're right about that," Ted agreed. "I'm glad it hasn't changed, too."

"You been gone long, Corporal? I mean, away from Ridgeway and this part of the country."

"Four years," Ted told the porter with a nod of his head. "And that's long enough, too."

"Where were you all that time? Way off on the other side of the world somewhere?"

"That's right. Africa. Italy. France."

"My, my! Maybe you won't be satisfied now to stay settled down in a little country town like Ridgeway after being in all those big places of the world."

154

"Don't you worry about that," Ted said with a quick jerking of his head. "I'm all ready to settle down for good, and there's no place like home for that."

Ted turned and looked out the window again. This time he could recognize familiar landmarks — landmarks that he had often thought about and had feared he would never see again. There was Churchman's Creek! And Palmer's farm! And the narrow dirt road to Jim Foster's house!

He caught his breath, his heart pounding painfully. The swiftly moving landscape was blurred and indistinct. He rubbed his eyes with the back of his hand.

"Jim," he said in a whisper, "Jim, I hate to be coming back like this without you."

At last the train was slowing down. Ted braced himself, eagerly watching the scattered houses on the outskirts as they came into view. Then suddenly there was the town itself.

There was the tall gaunt grain elevator — the high-fenced cattle-loading pen — the neat well-kept grassy lawns around the big gasoline storage tanks — there was everything in its place just as he had remembered hundreds of times during the past four years.

The brakes were grinding on the wheels and the porter was gently pushing him away from the vestibule door. Several other returning soldiers, most of whom he knew only vaguely, were crowding behind him on the narrow platform. Then the train stopped and the door was thrown open and the warm pungent odor of the land blew against his face.

Ted leaped to the ground, disregarding the two bottom steps, and felt his heels crunch into the loose gray gravel. Out of the mass of strange faces before him emerged four that he would have instantly recognized anywhere in the world. Before he could get to them, there came Mom and Dad, Sis and Tommy. His sister and younger brother fell against him, almost knocking him down in their eagerness to lock their arms around him. He could hear shouts and cries all around him as other soldiers leaped from the train.

Then he saw Mom running to him. She was weeping with joy and excitement.

"Teddy! Oh Teddy!" he heard her cry.

"Mom —" he murmured, hearing his own voice become husky and choked. He knew there were tears in his eyes by that time, but he did not feel ashamed of them now. "Mom, I sure am glad to be home —" He was sobbing so much by then that he was not able to finish what he was saying.

"Yes, Teddy!" she was saying over and over again. "Yes, Teddy! Yes, Teddy!"

When he looked up, blinking his eyes in the strong

156

morning sun, Henry Burton was standing there beside
him and smiling excitedly. Dad looked much older, and
his hair had grayed, but otherwise he had not changed
much.

"Dad —" Ted said, putting his arm around his father.
"Gee, Dad —"

He wanted to say something more — anything to let
his father know how glad he was to see him again after
all that time.

"Gee, Dad —" he said again.

A group of excited women rushed up to Ted and
pushed an armful of flowers at him. He took the flowers
awkwardly.

"We're welcoming all our heroes with flowers!" one
of the women said. "Welcome home, Corporal Burton!"

"But I don't want anything like this —" he tried to
protest.

The women had gone before he could stop them and
make them take back the flowers. He shoved the bou-
quet into his mother's arms.

"Mom, that's all wrong!" he said hoarsely. "I can't let
them treat me like a hero. They don't know what
they're doing. The real guys stayed over there, Mom.
They didn't come back. They're the heroes — those
guys over there. Jim Foster —"

"Now, Teddy, don't get upset," his mother said

soothingly, putting her hand on his arm. "Everybody means well. They're only trying to express gratitude to all the boys who are coming back home. Everybody knows some of them didn't come back —"

"But they don't understand, Mom. The guys who deserve all this — they're dead! Don't you understand, Mom? The real guys are dead! Tell them that, Mom! Don't let them keep this up! Stop them, Mom!"

Taking him by the arm, she led him gently to the automobile at the end of the station platform. Tears were streaming down his face and his body was shaking with sobs. He climbed blindly into the rear seat, and in an instant Towser, the big Husky dog, was leaping upon him. Towser licked Ted's tear-streaked face as Ted put his arms around him and hugged him.

"You understand, don't you, Towser?" he said, burying his face in the dog's heavy coat.

The dog yelped and barked, excited more than ever by the familiar sound of Ted's voice.

"You old rascal, you!" Ted said, locking the dog's body in his arms. "You old fuzzy-wuzzy, you! How do you remember me after all this time?"

He could feel Sis and Tommy crowding into the seat on either side of him.

"Boy, I sure missed you!" he said to Towser. "I sure wish you'd been with me. I got plenty lonesome out there a lot of times. What you been doing, boy? Chasing rabbits all over the country?"

"There are some of the girls you know, Teddy," he heard his mother saying. "You remember Florence Warren, don't you? And I think I saw Nancy Glennon just before the train came in. Don't you want to speak to them, Teddy?"

Shaking his head determinedly, he buried his face deeper into Towser's thick coat. Then he felt Mom pulling his arm. He sat up and looked around.

"Teddy, this is Mr. and Mrs. Foster — Jim's parents," she said. "They want to shake hands with you."

He stared dazedly at Mr. and Mrs. Foster. They were smiling kindly at him, and he could feel their hands gripping his.

"We're so glad you came back, Teddy," Mrs. Foster said. He could see tears brimming in her eyes, and he tried to keep from looking at her. "I know your parents are so proud of you and so glad to have you back home."

Mom closed the sedan door hurriedly, and Dad started the engine. They passed the little park in front of the courthouse and drove up a tree-shaded street. Then, before Ted realized what had happened, the car had come to a stop in front of a small white cottage. Sis and Tommy opened the doors and jumped out.

"Dad, why are we stopping here?" he asked, puzzled.

"Why, Teddy, this is where we live now," his mother told him. "This is home."

"Home?" he repeated, shaking his head.

"Yes, Teddy," she said gently. "We live here in town now. Two years ago —"

"But I didn't know —" he said, hesitating.

"Yes, Teddy. We've lived here about two years now. I wrote you all about it a long time ago. Don't you remember, Teddy?"

"No," he said dejectedly. "I guess I missed getting that letter. It must have got lost somewhere. And all the time I've been thinking — thinking about the farm —"

"The farm is still right where it's always been, son," Dad told him reassuringly. "Everything's just like it was when you went away. Nothing has changed. Everything's the same. I drive out there nearly every day to see how things are getting along. Everything's all right, son."

Ted got out of the car, followed by Towser at his heels, and went into the unfamiliar-looking house with his parents and Sis and Tommy. He could not tell them how disappointed he was, because he was afraid they would not understand.

"You'll get used to living here, son," Dad told him,

leading him into the small living room. "It's a lot more convenient for your mother here in town, and the children are nearer school. It's a lot better for everybody, everything considered."

"I know, Dad, but —"

"But what, son?"

"It's not — not —"

"Tell me what's wrong," his father said.

"Dad, it's not home — to me. I couldn't get used to living here."

Dad led him to the big chair by the window and pushed him down into it. He stood there patting Ted on the shoulder and smiling kindly.

"You're all tired out by the excitement, son," he said. "Just sit there and take it easy for a while. Everything will work out all right in the end. Now, stop worrying about things."

While Dad and Mom were telling him what had happened while he was away, Ted was gazing out the window. Instead of being able to see the broad dark fields stretching endlessly into the horizon, all he could see were small houses cramped close together on narrow lots and strange people walking along the street. He felt dejected and unhappy. He missed the tall barn jutting into the sky, the smell of the damp fields as the wind rustled the leaves of the oak trees, the endless rows of restless corn — he missed all the things he had thought about during all those years he was away.

The Norrises had moved to Kansas City, Mom was saying, and the Cutlers had bought a large farm. Sally Dowell was married to Frank Jones, and they had two small children. Tommy played shortstop on the junior baseball team at school, and Sis had won a first prize at the county homemaking fair. Fred Maxwell, who had been in Ted's class at high school, was vice president of the bank.

"But what about the farm?" Ted asked impatiently, unable to wait any longer. "Nothing has happened to the farm, has it, Dad?"

"Why, Teddy!" Mom said in surprise. "What's the matter, Teddy? Dad told you the farm is still there just like it's always been. You mustn't worry about it."

"I'm sorry, Mom," he said, relieved. "I just can't help it. I want to go out there — right away." He got up from the chair with a restless movement. "I can't stand it here. It's too crowded. The houses are too close together. Those people walking along the street out there — they're all strangers. They don't know what happened — they even look like they don't know what happened!"

"Happened where, Teddy?" she said tensely. "What do you mean?"

"Where I was!"

His father gripped his arm.

"Of course you can go out to the farm, son," he said calmly. "We'll drive out there as soon as we eat dinner. I'll bet you're hungry for some of your mother's cooking after all this time."

"I am, Mom," he said, smiling at her. "I sure am."

The car turned into the lane that led to the tall brown barn and the big white house under the oaks. Ted leaned forward, staring at the broad fields spreading away in all directions.

"Well, son, here we are," Dad was saying. "Does the old place look as good to you as you thought it would?"

"Better, Dad!" Ted said, nodding. "A lot better than I thought it would. It's the grandest sight in the world."

"You might be right about that, son," he agreed. "I sort of hated to leave the farm myself. But your mother had too much work to do out here. And she isn't as young as she was once, you know. I had to think of her, and that's why I decided we ought to move to town."

"That's right," Ted said. "Mom shouldn't work hard any more. She ought to take things easy now."

The car stopped under the tall oaks, and Ted got out. Towser barked until Ted opened the rear door of the sedan and let him jump to the ground. Everything, with the exception of Towser's yelping and barking, was quiet and serene.

Ed Fuller, who had lived there and helped run the farm ever since Ted could remember, hurried toward them from the barn. As soon as he recognized Ted in his uniform, he walked faster.

"Bless my soul!" Ed said, grasping Ted's hand and shaking it time after time. "I knew you'd come back, Teddy! Didn't I tell you that when you went away? Didn't I say nothing in the world could keep you from coming back home?"

"You were right about that, Ed," Dad said.

"It sure is good to be back and see you again, Ed," Ted told him. "I wish it had been a lot sooner."

"Now, that's where you're wrong, Teddy," Ed said sharply. He was once more the same old talkative and argumentative Ed Fuller. "If the war had been finished up any quicker than it was, it wouldn't have done the good it ought to have. The big thing about fighting a war is knowing how long to keep it going, not how soon you can stop it. Now, you take the generals on our side. They know their business, all right, because they didn't make the mistake of quitting and coming home the minute they saw we were winning. When you're fighting a man, you've got to keep it up till he won't want to fight any more. If you let him up on his feet as soon as he yells to quit, you'll have to whip him all over again some other time. Like I said, keeping it up as long as necessary is the smart way to fight one man or a million, and that's why our generals are the smartest in the world. If you asked around their home towns, you'd find out they learned how to scrap when they were kids tussling behind the schoolhouse at recess. I remember once when I was scrapping with a fellow . . ."

Later that afternoon, when it was time to drive back to town, Ted told his father that he wanted to stay at the farm for the night. Reluctantly, his father agreed, and he reminded Ted that there would be none of his mother's cooking to eat.

"All you'll get to eat out here will be Ed's beans," he said, shaking his head. "And it takes a brave man to make a meal of them. I know, because I've tried it."

"Now, look here," Ed protested. "Beans is the finest food a human can put in his stomach. I never would be able to do the work around here on this farm without a meal of beans. And if I ever have to stop eating beans, you can just get ready to find yourself another farmer to do the work."

The sun was setting when Henry Burton left the farm

and drove back to Ridgeway. Soon after that Ed went to the kitchen and made a fire in the stove. When Ted followed him inside a little later, Ed had an extra large pot of beans cooking. They sat at the kitchen table and talked a long time about the farm while they waited for the beans to be ready to eat.

"I don't know how you're going to like keeping batch out here with no womenfolks around," Ed said doubtfully when they began eating. "It's apt to get mighty lonesome for a young man your age. Why don't you set your mind to thinking about getting married, Teddy, if you want to stay out here? Of course, though, if you brought a woman here, you've got to remember that I'm not one to change my eating habits. I've still got to have my dish of beans three times a day."

"I'd see to it that you got plenty of beans, Ed," Ted promised. "Don't you worry about that."

"Does that mean you really are thinking about getting married, Teddy?" he asked. "Now, if you do, I've got it all figured out who it'll be. It's that Glennon girl over there beyond Churchman's Creek. I've remembered how sweet you were on her before you went away four years ago, and I don't reckon she'd forget, either. She ain't had a fellow at all since you left, and that's the best sign of all. When that happens, it means somebody is waiting for something. I see her every once in a while riding around

the farm over there on horseback, acting kind of lonesome and all. She sure did grow up to be a pretty girl,
Teddy. She's just about the prettiest girl around here,
and I mean in more ways than one . . ."

Ed was still talking when Ted got up and left the
kitchen.

Ted Burton was up early the next morning. He put
away his army uniform, folding it carefully and wrap-
ping it in paper to keep dust from reaching it. After that
he found some of his old clothes in a closet and put them
on. The clothes were tight, but they would do until he
could buy some new ones.

When Ted got to the kitchen, Ed served him a big
dish of warmed-over beans, and then he sat down and
watched Ted across the table. After eating some of the
beans, Ted pushed back his chair. Ed was concerned.

"Maybe you'd like them better with catsup poured
over them," Ed suggested, offering him the catsup
bottle.

"No," Ted said. "I guess I'm just not hungry this
morning."

"Maybe you had your fill of them in the army," Ed
said, shaking his head. "And if you don't want to eat
them, there's only one thing to do."

"What's that?"

"Get yourself married so you'll have a woman's cooking. There's no use thinking I'll do that kind of cooking for you, because I don't have the proper hang of it. It takes a female for that."

When they finished breakfast, they watered the stock and shelled corn in the barn and pitched fodder from the loft. After that Ted found some paint in the shop and began touching up the trim on the house. He was still working at mid-morning when a car stopped in the driveway. He climbed down the ladder, and just as his foot touched the ground he heard Nancy Glennon's voice. As he turned around, he saw her running toward him.

"Ted!" she cried, breathless and excited. "Ted! It's me! Nancy!"

His hands began to tremble, and he had to put the paint bucket on the ground.

"Don't you remember me at all, Ted?" she implored. "I'm Nancy, Ted! It's me!"

She came slowly toward him. When she stopped in front of him, Ted held out his hand instead of taking her into his arms as she had expected him to do. Nancy looked down at his hand in confusion.

"Ted, what's the matter?" she pleaded. "What's happened, Ted?"

He averted his eyes when he saw the look of disappointment on her face. He bit his lips uneasily.

"I'm — I'm glad to see you, Nancy," he said, still looking down at the ground.

"I don't understand, Ted," she said helplessly.

It hurt him so much to know that Nancy felt he was being unmerciful that he straightened up and looked into her face for the first time.

"I might have known something had happened," she was saying. "I might have known it when your letters stopped coming six months ago. Is it somebody else, Ted? Is that what has happened? Tell me the truth, Ted! I've got to know!"

"It's not easy to explain, Nancy," he managed to say. "I don't know how to —"

"Is it because you were injured in some way, Ted? Is that why you've forgotten?"

"No," he told her firmly. "I haven't forgotten a single minute, Nancy. It's nothing like that. I remember everything — not only about us — about other things, too. You remember Jim Foster, don't you, Nancy? Well, Jim Foster —"

"Of course I remember Jim," she said quickly. He knew she was trying to help him, but he wanted no help at a time like that. "But Ted, it's you I'm talking about."

"But Jim's got a lot to do with this, Nancy. You don't understand —"

"Look at me, Ted," she begged. He could see the bright smile on her face and he could feel her warm soft arms around his neck. "You remember what happened just before you went away, don't you, Ted?" she was saying. "We spent the whole day together at Churchman's Creek — just you and I alone. I brought a picnic basket and we . . ."

They were sitting under a shady tree on the bank of Churchman's Creek, and every once in a while he would put his arms around her and kiss her for a long time.

"There'll never be anyone else, Nancy — only you," he told her tenderly. "No matter what happens, that's what you must always remember. I love you, Nancy, and as soon as I get back from this war, we'll be married. You'll be waiting for me, won't you, Nancy? Say you will, Nancy! Please say you'll be waiting!"

"Of course I'll be waiting, darling," she told him, pressing her body close to his. "Don't ever for a second think anything else. I'm yours for always, Ted. Always and always yours."

Later in the afternoon a summer thunderstorm suddenly darkened the sky. Before they realized what had happened, their clothes were soaking wet from the

heavy shower. In a few minutes the sun was shining brightly again, and they took off their wet clothes and spread them on bushes to dry.

"It's a good time to take a swim in the creek while we wait," Nancy said.

"And we'd better watch our clothes," Ted said. "If somebody came along and took our clothes, we'd be in a jam."

After swimming and splashing in the water until they were thoroughly tired, they left the creek and stretched out on the grass in the sun.

"Do you know what we're going to do when I come back, Nancy?" he asked after a while.

"What, Ted?"

"Get married first, of course. And then —"

"And then what?" she said with a teasing smile.

"I'm serious, Nancy."

"And I am, too," she said, squeezing his hand. "Go ahead and tell me."

"We're going to have the finest stock farm anybody ever saw. Mostly horses, I think. Fine horses. Thoroughbreds."

"No cows, Ted?"

"Maybe a few. We'll need cows so we'll have milk and butter for the whatyoucallums."

"What's a whatyoucallum, Ted?" she said, smiling.

"Those little toddlers you see around a house."

"Ducks?"

"Ducks don't toddle. Ducks waddle."

"Oh, I know! You mean young calves and colts!"

"Maybe."

He tickled her nose with a blade of grass until she squirmed into his arms. They lay together while the sun sank slowly out of sight.

It was almost dark when they got up and dressed. As they walked toward Nancy's house, Ted put his arm around her.

"I'm leaving at six o'clock in the morning," he told her. "I won't see you again, Nancy."

She locked her arms around him desperately, clinging to him as though she would never let them be separated.

"Please don't say that, Ted!" she begged tearfully. "Please say you'll come back! Promise me you won't let anything happen to you — for our sake!"

"I didn't mean it that way, Nancy. Of course I'll come back. I'm coming back as sure as the sun will rise every morning while I'm away. Don't you see? Every time the sun comes up in the morning, it'll be a sign that I'm coming back."

"Yes, Ted. I'll remember that. I'll look at the sun every morning and remember exactly what you said.

And will you love me as much when you come back as you do now, Ted?"

"This is only the beginning, Nancy," he told her. "You just wait and see. The way I love you now is only a sample. You'll find out what I mean when I come back."

"Yes, darling," she said, pressing her lips against his. "Yes, darling . . ."

When he opened his eyes and looked at Nancy Glennon standing in front of him, his mouth was dry and his vision was blurred. He put his hands over his face and rubbed his eyes roughly. He was not surprised to see tears trickling down Nancy's cheeks, and it was all he could do to keep from taking her in his arms and begging her to forgive him for all the pain he had inflicted upon her.

Nancy turned and walked slowly toward her car in the driveway. He waited until she was opening the door, hoping she would turn around and say something to him — say anything, but not leave like that. He ran to the gate when he heard the engine start and saw the car turning around in the driveway.

"Nancy!" he called as the car moved away. "Nancy . . ."

That afternoon Mom and Dad, with Sis and Tommy in the rear seat, drove up the lane. Ted went to meet them as soon as the car stopped. Dad carried a large basket to the porch, and Mom had an armful of curtains which she took into the house.

"I baked some pies for you, Teddy," she told him. "They're in the basket with some fried chicken and some rolls I made for you. I knew you'd be hungry. Anybody would be if he had to live on Ed Fuller's beans three times a day."

Ted opened the basket and took out a piece of fried chicken. While he was eating, Mom was hanging the curtains over the windows and dusting off the furniture. Ted was so busy eating the chicken and rolls that he did not notice the change that had come over the room until he had finished.

"Why are you doing all that, Mom?" he asked, looking around the room. "You and Dad aren't moving back to the farm, are you?"

"No, Teddy," she told him with a shake of her head.

"Then why are you going to all this trouble, Mom?" he asked. "Ed and I can take care of the house. You shouldn't work like this."

"I've got to prepare the house, Teddy," she told him. "I wouldn't dream of letting anybody come here and find the place all dusty and dingy."

"Who's coming, Mom?"

She turned around and looked at him in surprise.

"Who's coming?" she repeated. "Why, Teddy! You know as well as I do."

He shook his head bewilderedly. "I don't know what you're talking about, Mom."

"Nancy, of course! Nancy Glennon! You and Nancy are going to be married, aren't you, Teddy?"

He shook his head at once. "No."

His mother sank heavily into a chair.

"What happened, Teddy? Nancy has been wearing the ring you gave her every minute since you left four years ago. Don't tell me that Nancy has broken the engagement! But only last week she told me —"

"Nancy didn't break the engagement, Mom. I did."

"You did! Why would you —"

"I just had to, Mom. That's the way it is. A lot of things have happened."

"But how could you, Teddy, after all this time? Nancy is such a wonderful girl — and she's waited all this time. What in the world will you do, Teddy?"

"I'm going to have the finest stock farm you've ever seen in your life, Mom," he told her earnestly. "I'm going to put in a new pasture along the creek and new fencing and get some blooded stock and —"

"Do you mean to tell me you are planning to do all

that, and still not marry Nancy Glennon?" She looked at him searchingly. "You mean you intend to stay out here on the farm all alone — just you and Ed Fuller?"

"I guess I'll be getting married, Mom. To somebody else."

"Somebody else?"

He nodded.

"Who, Teddy? Who in the world?"

"Florence Warren."

She stared at him, her eyes blinking from time to time.

"Florence Warren," she repeated presently. "I didn't know —"

"Of course, you didn't know, Mom," he told her. "It's something you didn't know anything about."

"But Florence Warren was engaged to Jim Foster, and they were to have been married if he hadn't been killed in the war —"

"Maybe that's why I'm asking her to marry me, Mom. Because Jim was killed —"

"But I don't understand, Teddy."

"I don't think anybody ever will understand, except Jim and me."

His mother looked at him in silence for a long time, and then she got up and began dusting energetically.

"Does Florence Warren know about this wild scheme of yours?" she asked severely.

"Not yet, Mom," he replied. "I haven't had a chance to ask her to marry me yet."

"Are you sure you're feeling all right, Teddy?" she asked with a worried frown.

"Sure," he said shortly. "I feel fine."

The next morning while he and Ed were shelling corn in the barn, Ted told him about his ideas for converting the place into a stock farm. Ed was gloomy-faced and unresponsive while Ted was talking. He shook his head to himself from time to time and said nothing until Ted had finished.

"Well, what do you think about that, Ed?" he asked. "Won't that make people sit up and take notice?"

"You'll have to get somebody else to take my place, Teddy," he replied firmly.

"Why, Ed?"

"Because I'm not the kind of dirt farmer who'll give up growing corn in the ground just to have it turned into feed for a pack of no-account horses. When I raise corn, I want to see it amount to some good in the world, like making meal for spoonbread, or mash for fattening hogs. It wouldn't make sense to me to spend all that time raising a barnful of corn just to see loafing horses eat it up. What good are those kind of horses, anyway? They don't do a lick of work. Sensible people these days want tractors and automobiles. Sensible people don't spend good sound money on a show horse that's only good for looks and nothing else."

"But I'm going to raise saddle horses, Ed. There's always a good market for saddle horses. We'll get some blooded stock and in a few years we'll have the finest horses that ever set foot on this country. Wouldn't it make you proud to know our horses were the best to be found?"

"Nope."

"You don't want to be a dirt farmer all your life, Ed. There are plenty of dirt farmers in the world already. If you listen to me, we'll be famous for our saddle horses. We'll win prizes at fairs and stock shows and things like that. Wouldn't that make you feel good?"

"Nope."

"Well, if that's the way you feel about it, I guess I'll have to look around for another partner. I hate to see you leave, though, because I've been counting on having you for my partner."

Ed kicked at a pile of corncobs, scattering them across the floor.

"Who said anything about leaving?" he demanded

angrily. "I've worked for your father about all my life, and no son of his is telling me to move off this farm. You can go ahead and raise your plugs and nags all you want to. I'll plant a crop somewhere on the farm where it won't interfere with your fine horses. But I'd better not catch one of them jumping fences and eating up my pea vines and grown corn. If I did catch one doing that, I'd shoot him dead and haul his carcass off to the rendering plant."

"That's more like it, Ed," Ted said. "You had me worried for a while."

After they had finished shelling the corn, Ted saddled one of the horses and rode off across the field. He went to the far side of the farm and looked at the land where he planned to put up new fencing for the grazing pasture. On the way back, he rode slowly along the hedgerow that marked the boundary of the Burton farm. On the other side of the hedgerow was the Glennon farm.

Ted drew up his horse and looked around when he heard hoofbeats somewhere nearby. Less than a hundred yards away he saw Nancy coming in his direction. Ted turned his horse around and waited.

It was only a few moments before Nancy recognized him, and she pulled her horse around sharply and rode off as fast as she could. Spurring his horse, Ted caught up with her at the far side of the field. Nancy refused to stop, or even to speak to him, and he had to reach for the reins and pull up her horse. Then he jumped to the ground.

"Nancy, I want to apologize for the way I behaved," he said. "I guess I was excited and didn't know what I was doing."

"You owe me no apology, Ted Burton," she said at once. "And that takes care of that." She tried to pull the reins from his grasp, but Ted would not release them. "Now that I mean nothing to you, it would be kind of you to turn my reins loose and let me go."

"But you've got to listen to me, Nancy," he said urgingly. "Please, Nancy."

"Why should I have to?" she asked coldly.

"Well, I mean, I want you to, Nancy."

She jumped to the ground and stood beside her horse. Ted, standing there so close to her, wanted to take her into his arms, but he felt that he had no right to touch her now.

"I don't know exactly how to say it, Nancy," he began uncertainly. "That's the hardest part — wanting to tell you and not knowing how to go about it."

"It's not even necessary to tell me anything, Ted," she said, relenting a little. There was a faint smile on her face for the first time. "I can see that I mean nothing to you any more. What else is there to say?"

"But that's not true, Nancy!" he protested.

"Then you certainly have developed a peculiar way of expressing what you mean. I suppose being in the war for four years has something to do with it. I've heard that some men never are the same again after that."

"But Nancy, you don't understand. I —"

"I believe I understand very well," she said quickly. "There's somebody else. Another girl —"

"Yes, but —"

"I don't believe I would be interested in listening to the intimate details." She turned and put one foot in the stirrup before he could stop her. He grasped her by the shoulders and turned her around. "Please don't touch me, Ted," she said evenly. "Please let me go."

"Not until I've told you something, Nancy," he said determinedly. "I love you, Nancy. I've loved you every minute while I was away. You believe me, don't you?"

Nancy covered her face with her hands. He could see her shaking her head as though she were weak and exhausted.

"But you've got to believe me, Nancy," he implored. "You've just got to believe me!"

"I don't have to believe anyone who says he loves me, but admits that there is somebody else," she said. "I never heard of such a thing! I suppose this is one of the peculiar ideas you picked up in your travels about the world. But whatever it is, Ted Burton, I want nothing to do with it."

"Maybe it does sound peculiar back here at home," Ted said, staring across the dark field. "Maybe people back here at home will never understand some of the things that happened over there in the war, where you'd be laughing and joking with your buddies one second, and then all of a sudden you'd look around and see them bleeding to death and know they were too far gone to help and that there was nothing you could do but stay with them until they were dead. At a time like that I guess you do get some peculiar notions about life, but somehow it didn't matter how peculiar your notions might sound to people back home. They'd never understand what you went through at a time like that. All you knew was that your pal, who had gone through hell with you, was dead. That puts a queer feeling into any man."

Nancy sat down beside the hedgerow. The two horses, standing side by side now, began nibbling at the grass.

"That's what happened to Jim Foster," Ted was saying. "Before we went away in the army, we went to school together and wrestled in the barn on Saturdays and got mad at each other and went fishing together on Sundays. Jim was the best pal I ever had. There was one time over there when we were in a tough spot, and Jim saved my life. He didn't have to, but he did. He saved my life, and it cost him his life. If it hadn't been for Jim Foster, I wouldn't be alive now. I wouldn't be here talking to you. People can't understand things like that. That's why they think the ones who come back are heroes. The heroes didn't come back."

Ted took a cigarette from his pocket and lit it with trembling fingers.

"That night in Italy," he said, taking a deep breath. "That's when it was. We had been up at the front for a week, and it was in the middle of winter with deep snow covering everything. Jim received orders to take a five-man patrol through the lines and bring back some prisoners for questioning. It was important to get those prisoners to find out what the other side was up to. I went with Jim . . ."

Night was closing in when they left the advanced post and began crawling through the deep snow toward the German lines. It was rough mountainous country, and the snow was three or four feet deep in some places. German shells bursting on the slope of the mountain made scarlet splotches in the snow — like splattered blood.

When they reached the ravine near the German lines,

they slid down the slope and made their way up the opposite side. Machine gun fire was incessant, and they could hear spent bullets whirring out of the starless sky.

They succeeded in going several hundred yards deep into the German positions, and Jim Foster decided they had gone far enough. He disappeared for nearly half an hour, leaving Ted in charge of the patrol, and when he returned, he told them that he had spotted a group of half a dozen Germans manning a machine gun post.

The patrol surrounded the post and took the Germans by surprise. The Germans expected to be shot, and when they realized they were being taken prisoner, they willingly surrendered their arms and started crawling down the side of the ravine.

Then, deep in the ravine, the patrol and its prisoners ran into a much larger German patrol. A dozen grenades were thrown, and Jim and Ted, together with two of the prisoners, were the only ones left alive. Knowing that the German patrol outnumbered them, but being determined to get the two remaining prisoners through the lines, Jim ordered Ted to take the prisoners through the other end of the ravine while he held the German patrol off. A moment later a grenade fell nearby, and Jim was hit.

"I guess it's all over for me, Ted," Jim said weakly. "That grenade got me."

"We'll give up, Jim," Ted told him. "You'll get first aid, and you'll be all right. Being a prisoner of war in Germany won't be too bad."

"No," Jim said, "we can't do that. You've got to get those two prisoners back to the captain."

"But you'll die here, Jim. You won't live half an hour, bleeding the way you are. Let's give up and get first aid while there's time."

While he was talking, Ted was ripping his uniform into strips and trying to stop the flow of blood.

"Now, get going," Jim ordered. "There'll be more grenades coming in here any second, and they'll get all of us. I don't want those prisoners to get killed. The captain needs them. I'll keep firing as long as I can, and by that time you'll be out of the ravine. Now, get going like I tell you, Ted."

"Jim, I'm going to call out there and say we'll surrender."

"You open that mouth of yours, and I'll shoot you, Ted. So help me God, I'll shoot you dead!"

"Listen, Jim," Ted pleaded. "We won't lose this war just because a couple of guys give up when we're surrounded and you're bleeding to death. You know what the captain would say. He'd say we did the right thing. They don't expect us to commit suicide if we can't bring back a couple of prisoners."

"We don't give up that easy in this army, pal," Jim said weakly. "We carry out an order until it's counter-manded. And you don't see those flashy guys on shiny motorcycles coming up the ravine with orders for us to come back without prisoners or surrender, do you? No, by God! We were sent out here to get as many pris-oners as we could between sunset and sunrise, and the night's not over by a damn sight. I'm staying here, and you're taking those prisoners to the captain. Under-stand?"

"But they'll kill you, Jim!"

"So what? If you stayed here, they'd kill you, too."

"Then we'll carry you back. Those two prisoners can do it."

"No, you won't. The minute those Germans out there found out we'd left, they'd catch up with us and get us all. I'm staying here and pecking away at them as long as I've got something to shoot."

Several more grenades exploded nearby. The Ger-mans were on three sides of them by then, and they would soon be surrounded.

"Do one thing for me, Ted," Jim said. "I want only one favor."

"Sure, sure! What is it, Jim. I promise on my word of honor to do anything in the world you want."

"All right, I'll tell you what it is, Ted. I've got a girl

back home — Flo Warren. You know all about that. She's got my ring, and we were going to get married the minute I set foot in Ridgeway. I know you've got a girl — Nancy. But Ted —"

"What about Flo Warren, Jim? Go ahead and tell me. I'll do whatever it is you want. I swear I'll do anything in the world you say, Jim."

"Take care of her for me, Ted. That's all. She's my girl, and when I die, I'll die loving her. Tell her I tried to come back and get married, but I couldn't make it. Tell her I had to stay here. I'm afraid she'll marry somebody who'll mistreat her, Ted. I don't want that to happen when I'm dead and can't do anything about it. That's why I want you to take care of her. Look after her, Ted. See that she doesn't marry somebody who'll mistreat her. If you didn't have Nancy, I'd ask you to marry Flo. Then I'd know she'd never have a tough time of it. If that could happen, I'd be satisfied. I'd never have to worry again. But I couldn't ask you to do that. You've got Nancy waiting at home for you."

Jim got to his knees and fired his gun in the direction of the Germans. Several more grenades came hurtling through the night and exploded near them. The two German prisoners huddled close to Jim and Ted.

"Hurry and get going, Ted," Jim ordered. "Get out of here. If you don't, I'll turn my gun on you. I'm still in command of this patrol, and you're going to obey me or I'll have to shoot you. Now, get out!"

Jim shoved his gun into Ted's ribs. By then Ted realized it would be useless to try to argue with Jim any more, and he crawled through the snow toward the end of the ravine, prodding the prisoners ahead. When they reached the end of the ravine, they began crawling up the steep slope. Once he heard the sound of Jim's gun, and he looked down into the ravine. At that moment there were violent flashes of light when dozens of grenades exploded, making the night as bright as day. After that, Jim's gun remained silent.

Ted, prodding the two prisoners up the slope, did not look back again.

There were tears in Nancy's eyes. He felt the touch of her hand on his.

"I don't know what to say, Ted." Her voice was low and almost indistinct. "I know how you feel. But I don't know what to say."

They got up and stood beside the horses.

"I'd counted so much on coming back to you, Nancy," he was saying to her. "Nobody in the world knows what it means to me. I'd thought about marrying you and living here on the farm together — that's all I did think about. But I can't forget Jim Foster. And if he hadn't sent me away that night in Italy, I wouldn't be here now. And when you think about it a lot, the way I do, you get to thinking Jim wasn't the only one, either. Thousands of guys died the way he did, and that's why I came back alive. I just can't let Jim down now. I just can't do it."

"I know," Nancy said softly. She brushed the tears from her eyes. "I understand now, Ted. I think I do, anyway."

The late afternoon sun fell brightly upon the carpet at Flo Warren's feet. During all the time that Ted had been pacing up and down the floor, she had not moved. When he finished telling her about the night in the ravine, he crushed out his cigarette and stopped in front of her.

"He was the greatest guy that ever lived, Flo," Ted said solemnly. "He could have let us surrender to the Germans, but he knew the captain needed information from the prisoners. He could have let us carry him out of the ravine, but he knew the Germans would have caught up with us and killed us both. Jim wanted one of us to come back home, and he figured I had the better chance of getting out of there alive."

He sat down on the sofa beside her, twisting his fingers nervously and watching them intently as though he expected them to say the things he wanted to say.

"After knowing Jim, I'm afraid you won't be very happy with me," he said presently, still looking down at his hands.

Flo looked at him with a quick turning of her head.

"But I'm not going to marry you, Ted," she said quietly. "I wouldn't for anything in the world."

"But Jim said —"

Shaking her head, she got up and went to the desk on the other side of the room. Opening a drawer, she took out a neatly tied stack of letters. When she found a particular envelope, she brought it to the sofa.

"No, Ted," she said calmly. "I knew Jim, and slowly, I'm beginning to know him a lot better — even better than you do. Here's a letter that Jim wrote to me a long time ago. It was soon after he landed in Italy. He wrote me that no matter what happened — even if he died over there — he wanted me always to be friendly — that's how he said it — friendly with you and Nancy. At that time I thought it was strange he would say something like that. Or maybe it was because I didn't want to know what he meant. Maybe I didn't even want to think that he could — could —"

"Expect?" Ted spoke up.

She nodded quickly.

"Yes. That's it exactly. I didn't even want to think

that he could expect me to know what he meant. But that's what he wanted me to understand. He wanted me to know that without him, he expected me to be friendly with you and Nancy. He didn't want me to become bitter and resentful toward you and Nancy if I found out he sacrificed his life to save yours. He didn't want my bitterness to spoil the lives of any of us — yours or Nancy's or mine. And it won't, Ted. Please believe me. Jim knew that when the time came I'd know — and he wrote to me in such a way that I had to know and understand — what to do. That's why he asked you to come to me, Ted. He knew I could explain things a lot better than he could at a time like that."

Nancy was waiting when Ted drove his car into the Glennon driveway and got out. She ran to him, reaching the gate at the same moment he did. And she knew as soon as she saw his face that he would not have to tell her that he had come back to her. Before a word was spoken, he reached over the gate and put his arms around her.

"A lot of people in this town will never realize what Jim Foster did for them," he said. "I wish there were some way to make them understand — like Flo Warren does. They think he was just one of the guys who got killed in the war because he was careless or because it was an accident. They don't know there were other ways to die in the war. Jim died, all right, but if they put up a monument to him sky-high, it still wouldn't be big enough for a guy like him. We're going to remember that, Nancy, as long as we live."